THE SKIN OF THE EARTH

By the same Author

CLIMATOLOGY

THE SKIN OF THE EARTH

by

AUSTIN MILLER

D.Sc.

Professor of Geography in the
University of Reading

With 67 Illustrations

METHUEN & CO. LTD. LONDON

36 Essex Street, Strand, W.C.2

First published in 1953

c

1.1

CATALOGUE NO. 4257/U

PRINTED IN GREAT BRITAIN BY
BUTLER AND TANNER LTD., FROME AND LONDON

6002450545

PREFACE

THIS book is the outcome of a two-year course in practical Physical Geography given to Honours and General Degree students of Geography in their second and third years at the University of Reading. It is built on the foundations of a first-year course in the Physical Basis of Geography which includes practical work on relief maps and weather maps, and it assumes that the reader is already familiar with the elements of these subjects. It is, therefore, no substitute for the manuals of elementary map work that are abundantly available, but begins where most of them leave off.

First-year work at a University must be mainly concerned with description and explanation from close inspection of the map, second- and third-year work is concerned with analysis and derivation. Techniques are here presented for sorting and sifting the facts that map and statistics abundantly record in highly condensed form, and for extracting, if not the last ounce of information they contain, at least a great deal that escapes even the most observant eye.

I am indebted to Professor S. W. Wooldridge for his encouragement and his reading of the typescript, to Mr. M. Parry who has recently shared in conducting the classes and has also read and improved the typescript, to successive Student Demonstrators who have helped with the supervision of the classwork on which the book is based, and to some twenty-five years of students who have worked the exercises with varying degrees of patience and skill.

CONTENTS

CHAP.   PAGE

PREFACE   V

1. PRINCIPLE AND PRACTICE   I

PART I. TOPOGRAPHICAL ANATOMY

2. SKIN STRUCTURE: THE GEOLOGICAL MAP   9

    Section I. Geological structures   11

    Section II. Examination by sections   28

3. SURFACE MORPHOLOGY: THE RELIEF MAP   43

    Section I. The analysis of slope   46

    Section II. The analysis of shape   74

PART II. THE CIRCULATORY SYSTEMS

4. THE AIR: ITS MOVEMENT AND PHYSICAL STATE   91

    Section I. The daily round: Weather maps and diagrams   91

    Section II. The long-term plan: Climatic maps and data   113

5. THE WATER CIRCULATION: RAINFALL AND HYDROLOGY   148

    Section I. Ingestion. The analysis of precipitation   148

    Section II. Metabolism. The function of water   162

    Section III. Excretion. The disposal of water   178

POSTSCRIPT   196

INDEX   197

ILLUSTRATIONS

FIG.   PAGE

1. Determination of dip from relation of outcrop to contours   15
2. Stratum contours on the 'Chalk Rock'. Aylesbury sheet   16
3. Simple geometry of dip, thickness, and outcrop width   17
4. Causes of symmetrical repetition of outcrop   18
5. Limiting cases of width of outcrop   19
6. Development of outcrop from given direction and amount of dip   20
7. Three-point method of developing outcrop   22
8. Outcrop of bed, dipping into hill and downhill   23
9. Sectioned dome   24
10. Dip fault traversing a syncline, uneroded and eroded   25
11. Unconformity   26
12. Unconformity with overlap   26
13. Unconformity: map and section   31
14. Unconformity on undulating surface   31
15. Overlap. Based on Marlborough sheet   32
16. Geological map with errors   34
17. Geologist's field map   35
18. Igneous rocks. Penzance sheet   37
19. Relative age of igneous rocks   38
20. Template of standard contour spacings   47
21. Determination of average slope   48
22. Thalweg profiles of the River Wye and tributaries   52
23. Former thalweg reconstructed from transverse profiles across a rejuvenated valley   55
24. Valley-in-valley form and knick-points   56
25. Construction of projected profile   57
26. Projected profiles: (a) Side view: Interfluve profiles west of Lampeter–Carmarthen road. (b) Front view: North of the Severn Estuary between the Usk and the Wye   59
27. Staggered spur profiles. Mawddach Estuary   61
28. Amplitude of relief: River Rhymney   62
29. Available amplitude of relief   63
30. Generalized contours   64
31. Reconstructed extent of marine platforms   66
32. Estimating area by sampling along parallel lines   67
33. Hypsometric curve and area-height curve   71
34. Altimetric frequency curves (modified from Baulig)   73
35. Thickness of limestone. Karstic drainage   75
36. Hydrographic network; climatic control   76
37. The hierarchy of divides in south-east England   77
38. Divides, gaps, and captures, Southern Ireland   79
39. Construction of one-point perspective   81
40. Construction of two-point perspective   82
41. Section in perspective   83

FIG.   PAGE
42. Some conventionalized relief forms on block diagrams   85
43. Home-made sketching frame and V-sight pinned to a plane table 86
44. Weather observation stations. Kew model plotted   97
45. Isotherms at 4° F. intervals overdrawn on a weather map   101
46. Piecemeal analysis of the station model   103
47. Use of geostrophic scale for determining wind velocity   104
48. Use of geostrophic scale for estimating travel of fronts   106
49. Sample ascent plotted on simplified height diagram   108
50. Skeleton quograph with some conversion lines   116
51. Reliability of winds in the North Atlantic (July)   119
52. Temperature dispersion graph. Daily maximum (+) and minimum
        (—) at Reading University, 1950   130
53. Annual rise and fall of temperature compared   135
54. Climatic stations and the limit of trees in sub-arctic North America 141
55. Determination of the date of crossing a temperature threshold 145
56. Hydrographic cycle   149
57. Climographs (after Griffith Taylr)   163
58. Hythergraphs   164
59. Winter rain and average yield of wheat in Victoria (Australia),
        1890–1914. Formula of a straight line   168
60. Temperature, rainfall, and yield of wheat in Europe   172
61. Limits of forest, grassland, and desert   173
62. Nomogram for estimating effective temperature   175
63. Mean monthly evaporation values at Campden Hill and Southport,
        calculated from formula   180
64. Catchment area of the River Exe   184
65. Cross-sectional area of stream beds   187
66. Rainfall–discharge relationship. River Severn at Bridgnorth   192
67. Solution of Fig. 17   193

A piece of transparent squared paper which will simplify the reading of graph diagrams will be found at the end of the book

CHAPTER I

PRINCIPLE AND PRACTICE

ANALOGY is a dangerous device and has been known to cause more confusion than clarity of understanding. The risks are diminished, however, when the listener is already familiar with the elements of the concept to be explained, and as this book is intended for those who have enjoyed a long familiarity with the surface of the map, at school or in the open air, I venture to state my aim in the form of two analogies. Since these are taken from fields of learning as far apart as the art of music and the science of anatomy there is little danger that they can be taken too literally.

The Symphony of Landscape

The landscape has been compared to a symphony whose various elements, subtly interwoven, combine to assault the senses with a pleasure of fine sound. If this is so then a map is to the landscape as the printed score is to the symphony. The character that these two media of expression possess in common is that both sound and form, appealing directly to the eye and to the ear respectively, can be represented and recorded on a piece of paper only diagrammatically and by means of a system of conventional signs. To enjoy the interplay of harmonies and rhythm most of us must hear the symphony played by a full orchestra; to appreciate the blending of its elements we must go out and view the landscape. But a trained musician with the score before him as he sits in an easy chair can hear the music in his mind's ear; a trained geographer poring over the map can see the landscape in his mind's eye. Neither faculty is a heaven-sent gift, but is acquired by methodical study and long practice. The musician dissecting the piece, examining the function of the strings, the brass or the woodwind, following the motifs and their development and analysing the harmonies, appreciates how the interplay of the lines produces the combined effect. The geographer, likewise, called upon to analyse the landscape and to assume the role of reporter or critic in interpreting it to the public, must make a careful study of the parts before he can appreciate the whole. Whether he assumes this office with diffidence, with modesty, with confidence or with overweening conceit, the assumption lays upon him the duty of understanding each and all of the instrumental lines that blend together in the oneness of the landscape.

It is a valuable experience, perhaps an indispensable one, for a musical critic to have helped to make music as an individual instrumentalist in an orchestra, for in this discipline he had learnt his craft from the inside and come to understand how his own instrument's contribution, incomplete and unsatisfying in itself, helps to build up the effect. He has compelled himself grimly to focus his attention on his own part, refusing firmly to permit his concentration to be distracted by all the other fascinating things that are going on around him.

It is an equally valuable experience for the regional geographer, aiming eventually to interpret the landscape in its entirety, to have made himself thoroughly competent in at least one of its specialist disciplines; the apprenticeship to the important and responsible office of jack-of-all-trades should include the mastery of at least one. It is perhaps too much to ask that he should make himself master of all, but at least he must have a knowledge of the techniques of all, a sympathetic understanding of their problems and the power to assess their contribution to the composition. Nature and man have collaborated to compose the landscape and though the planner may be called upon to edit or rewrite it, the geographer plays the role of reporter and critic; he is an unreliable critic who does not understand the science and the art of composition.

Discordant Themes

It is worth repeating, for it is fundamental, that nature and man have collaborated in the composition; the collaboration has not often been successful and the consequence is frequently a contrapuntal cacophony. Herein is revealed the unsoundness of the analogy we have been pursuing, for a musical work is the creation of one brain, is purposefully designed and has a coherence of its parts, and even if its harmonies are 'modern' or experimental a trained musician can detect the purpose and the principle on which it is built. But the landscape has become what it is without the exercise of any conscious control by a single creator. Certainly in the process of its gradual evolution some 'harmony' will have resulted from the natural laws that have operated to produce the land forms, and the natural vegetation will be 'in harmony' with the climate and soils. But the combination of features, though they are causally related, need not present a harmonious impression in the eye of the observer. Not every natural scene is beautiful; often it is dreary, desolate or downright ugly and, in the aesthetic sense, its elements may seem to shriek discordantly and its colours to clash. But in so far as it is a 'natural' landscape its structure and form are comprehensible to the eye of one trained in physical geography.

Such natural landscapes are only to be found in uninhabited parts of the globe; elsewhere man has left his mark and created a variety of artificial landscapes. His crops, hedges, and trees, quarries, roads, reservoirs, houses and towns have overlaid the natural scene or even completely supplanted it, sometimes with an eye to beautification but more often not, sometimes with a pattern designed in conformity with nature but more often incongruously.

Thus the interpretation of landscape, which is the business of the geographer, demands first an understanding of how the natural scene has come into being (this is physical geography) and next an understanding of the pattern that the hand of man has laid upon the face of the earth (this, broadly, is human geography).

'The Unique Nature of Regions'

Most geographers are now agreed that their proper sphere is the study of the surface of the earth as the home of man, but since man is subjected to a bewildering variety of influences, physical, biological, economic, political, and historical, the study of the milieu in which he finds himself becomes a highly complicated exercise in the 'integration of the sum total of phenomena' in the 'region'. This, no less, is the aim of regional geography; but it is disturbingly apparent that so many variables, each with an almost infinite possibility of variation, will never combine in identical ways in two regions, and that no two regions can be exactly alike in all respects. We are bound to recognize, therefore, that regional geography must be individually descriptive and that any comparison or classification of regions is possible only in respect of their broad similarities. Herbertson's natural regions are of this nature, but they presume to do no more than classify the natural environment out of which man, by varying his cultural, historic, economic, political, and other activities, may call into existence a varied assortment of living conditions.

System in Physical Regions

Only by rigidly limiting the number of variables can we hope to arrive at a classification of regions that can have any validity. Thus a classification of climatic regions is possible and the comparable regions can be defined with a fair degree of precision, because the elements of climate are limited in number and, to some degree, interrelated. The orderly arrangement and presentation of phenomena in this way is one of the aims of the scientific method and in this sense climatology presents greater opportunity for scientific treatment than any other branch of geography.

Similarly geomorphology, confining its attention to the form of the land and ignoring vegetational, animal and human phenomena, can devise a satisfying classification of land forms based on their structure, mode of origin and stage in evolution. These two branches of geographical knowledge, together with oceanography, constitute the 'Physical Basis of Geography' whose findings receive a satisfactory explanation in the operation of physical laws, and it is with them that this book is concerned. The author's aim is to encourage a scientific treatment of that part of the field of geography that is most amenable to the scientific method, and within this limited field to insist on objective methods of examination which are in accordance with the practice and discipline of the sciences. Such methods are more difficult to apply in human or regional geography and less progress has up to the present been made in devising suitable techniques.

My aim, therefore, is to collect and present techniques which may be applied, quite objectively, to arrive at conclusions whose validity is as far as possible free from suspicion of personal bias and preconceptions.[1]

The Value of Practical Methods

The starting-points for each exercise in this book are the true facts objectively determined by the surveyors of the land and the observers of the weather and climate; the treatment to which they are subjected must also be objective. The method of their treatment is practical and, in the practice, the student can hardly fail to find out for himself facts that would have escaped him had he taken the generally accepted conclusions for granted. At the same time he will become uncomfortably aware, as he wrestles with the figures or the maps, of limitations in the data and of weaknesses in the line of argument that he would cheerfully have accepted had he not been compelled to enquire into their adequacy and logical sequence.

As an educational principle there is considerable merit in the self-discipline imposed by practical work. There exist, I believe, a fortunate few endowed with the gift of learning as they read without apparent effort, but their armchair methods of working are more to be envied than emulated; for the average student the labour involved in making notes on what he hears and abstracts of what he reads amply repays the time and labour spent, for the effort forcibly enlists the understanding and the understanding aids the memory. The value of the principle of learning by doing is accorded recognition in the 'sciences' by the universal insistence on practical work, a discipline in which progress, though slow, is very thorough. Geography, as a subject aspiring to recognition as a science, must make every effort to use this valuable method to its fullest advantage.

The data of meteorology are the figures of pressure, temperature, humidity, precipitation, sunshine, &c. recorded under standard conditions; averages of such figures over a period of time comprise the data of climate and these may be presented in tabular or in map form. The precise data of geomorphology are the surveyor's measurements and these are nearly always presented in map form. Whether this immense

[1] An outline of these techniques and a discussion on their merits was given in a Presidential Address to the Institute of British Geographers ('The Dissection and Analysis of Maps', *Trans. Inst. Brit. Geog.*, 1948).

volume of factual information is presented as tables of figures or by means of the map, it fully deserves the most careful inspection and examination, but all too frequently the student proceeds no further than inspection and comment, stopping short just where they begin to yield their treasures. The map, in fact, is a mine of information, but only a fraction of the information is lying around waiting to be picked up. The richer deposits must be dug out, 'panned' and concentrated if the mine is to be worked efficiently and economically. Careful analysis, arrangement, and treatment can extract from the data on the map a wealth of information, all too often unsuspected; but the technique of this analysis has to be learnt.

Anatomy and physiology of the skin of the earth

This brings me to my second analogy, that of the 'anatomy' and 'physiology' of the living skin of the earth. The anatomy of landscape, like any other anatomy, can only be learnt by careful dissection, limb by limb, organ by organ, following each sinew or nerve with meticulous care. Maps, being man-made, can hardly be said to have an anatomy, but they may be regarded as diagrams of the anatomy of landscape, from which much may be learnt about the carcase itself. Meteorological charts and maps show the physiological state of the the skin of the earth, its temperature, its moisture, and the circulation of air and water in it and upon it. Precise measurements of these physical states are available in the abundant, though often unsatisfactory, data that meteorologists have compiled.

It is on this analogy that the title and chapter headings have been chosen for this book; methods not unlike those of anatomical dissection and physiological experiment will be applied and techniques explored for revealing the structure and functioning of the skin of the earth. Space and the embryonic stage yet reached in these investigations only permit the treatment of some of the better known and most revealing methods, but if the application of the operations here described succeeds in opening up a vista of possibilities it will have fulfilled its purpose, which is not so much to teach any geology, geomorphology, meteorology climatology, or hydrology as to present examples of devices by which these sciences, contributory to the full art of the geographer, may be studied.

The significance of the facts that will be disinterred from the map or discovered from statistical data by following the treatment prescribed lie beyond the scope of this book. It must be assumed that the reader is already well acquainted with physical geography and can appreciate the significance of such things as reversed faults, density of drainage pattern, temperature anomalies, or the variability of rainfall. Nor will it be possible to follow up the implications in human and economic geography of such things as faulting of coal-seams, a fall-line on rivers, run-off and percolation factors, or the correlation between climatic values and the yield of crops. The main purpose is to suggest methods of detecting, displaying, and assessing evidence which is not immediately apparent from a superficial inspection of maps and figures. The use to which that evidence is put must be the concern of the reader.

PART I
TOPOGRAPHICAL ANATOMY

CHAPTER 2

SKIN STRUCTURE:
THE GEOLOGICAL MAP

THE skin of the earth is very thin and consists of layers of sedimentary rocks, except where igneous rocks of deep-seated origin have burst through the crust or been laid bare by long-continued erosion. The composition, structure, and disposition of these rocks strongly influence the evolution of relief in the early stages of the cycle of erosion, though their control becomes progressively less and less conspicuous as the cycle proceeds towards the 'peneplain' stage of old age. The behaviour of each lithological type of rock should be known and can be found from any text-book of geology but there are some pitfalls for those who use geology without understanding it. For example, most geological mapping is now based on age of rocks rather than on lithology, but many lithological terms have survived with a new connotation. Thus what is mapped as Old Red Sandstone is not always red and is frequently not a sandstone. Rocks with the same name, e.g. the Hythe Beds of the ' Lower Greensand ', may have very different composition (and hardness) even over quite small distances of the same outcrop. The explanation of relief in terms of geology is not a simple matter that can be read with any certainty from the map alone. Nevertheless the map, succinctly recording the findings of the field geologist, has much to tell; but it is necessary first to know the grammar of the language in which it is written.

Geological Maps

The geological information contained in a geological map is usually superimposed on a standard topographic map; the Geological Survey, for example, makes use of the uncoloured base maps supplied by the Ordnance Survey and prints thereon the outcrop of each formation, together with much other geological information such as dip, faults, and mineral veins. The symbols and the cartographic methods used in different surveys vary slightly, but the essential principles are the same in all cases. The maps of the Geological Survey of England, Wales, and Scotland will be used for illustration in the chapters that follow, and once these are known the student will have no difficulty in understanding any other official or unofficial geological map.

The following maps are available:

1. 6 in. = 1 mile. Except in regions of very complicated geology the original map is now prepared by the field geologist on this scale

9

which forms the basis for all maps on smaller scales. These maps are not generally on sale, but may be copied or consulted at the Geological Survey and Museum in Exhibition Road.

2. 1 in. = 1 mile. The most important and most useful of the series. Old and New series (see below) 'Drift' and 'Solid' editions.

3. ¼ in. = 1 mile. 'Drift' and 'Solid' editions. Fewer subdivisions can be shown on this map because of its smaller scale, but it forms a useful basis of broad regional analysis.

4. 10 miles = 1 in. Sheet 1, Scotland and N. England. Sheet 2, Rest of England and Wales. One of a series produced by the (then) Ministry of Town and Country Planning.

5. 25 miles = 1 in. A useful general map showing at a glance the broad geological structure of the British Isles.

The Geological Survey was formed in 1835 and its early maps were made by simply colouring the 1-in. topographic maps of the day. Later the geology was engraved on the black-and-white small sheet hachured map. This method, with refinements, was followed until the whole country was covered and the maps made available as the 'Old Series, hand-coloured'. By the time revision began the advance of geological science and the demand for detailed information in certain areas where geology is of economic importance had made it possible and desirable to work in greater detail, and the 6-in. scale was adopted for field work (in some areas of complicated structure even larger scales were adopted). The information was then reduced to the 1-in. scale for publication, and in 1893 the New Series (colour printed) began to appear, the base map being the small sheet series (18 in. × 12 in.) black outline map. Large blocks of the country were completed and the maps issued before the Second World War, but all existing stocks were destroyed by enemy action. A list of sheets reissued since the war can be obtained from the Geological Survey.

Section I. Geological Structures

Vertical Succession of Rocks

It is an inevitable limitation of the geological map, as of all maps, that only the surface distribution, or outcrop, of each bed can be shown, but it may be important to know what lies beneath at any depth. In time such a degree of familiarity and expertness will be attained that one can, from a brief study of the map, answer this question, but until that stage is reached the student must have recourse to section drawing, which thus becomes a very important, in fact an essential, exercise. All geological maps nowadays include a section, but this only reveals the structure along some line drawn across the map; anywhere else the section must be visualized or drawn.

The order of superposition of the beds present on each sheet is given in the legend or key at the side of the map. In the older maps the order alone was given and each bed was shown by a coloured block of uniform height, but in all the newer sheets the vertical succession is drawn to approximate scale of thickness, and the thicknesses are given. Of course it often happens that the thickness of a given formation is variable over the area shown on the map and in this case the scale of the legend cannot be exact, but where this variation is significant the fact will be indicated in the legend by means of a tapering block of the conventional colour of that formation.

It will be noticed that the colours used for each formation are now standardized; thus shades of brown and grey are used for the Eocene, shades of green and blue-green for the Cretaceous, and complicated colour effects are obtained by cross hatchings in colours on a ground of some other shade. But the great number of formations to be represented and the limited number of colours available make it inevitable that two colours, distinguishable only with difficulty, may sometimes have to be used for two formations even on the same map; in this case a distinction can be made by reference to the key letter and figure which is printed both in the legend and on the outcrop.

These key letters and figures are again standard on all modern maps as follows:

a Cambrian	*f* Triassic
b Ordovician and Silurian	*g* Jurassic
c Devonian	*h* Cretaceous
d Carboniferous	*i* Tertiary
e Permian	

These are subdivided by numbers, thus:

h^1 Weald Clay h^4 Upper Greensand
h^2 Lower Greensand h^5 Chalk
h^3 Gault

These in turn may be subdivided by dashes, thus:

$h^{5'}$ Lower Chalk $h^{5'''}$ Upper Chalk
$h^{5''}$ Middle Chalk

Other alphabets and symbols are used for 'drifts', pre-Cambrian rocks, igneous and metamorphic rocks. They are always printed in the legend.

It will be observed that the Silurian and Ordovician share the key letter b. This is because these two formations were not separated in the early days of the Geological Survey; in fact the Ordovician was not recognized as a distinct system until 1879. Formerly the term Silurian was applied to all rocks between the then Cambrian and the Devonian. Similarly i is used for both Eocene and Oligocene, not separately recognized when the key letters were decided upon.

In the stratigraphical tables given above the nomenclature of beds often appears to be based on the type of rock (sandstone, clay, or chalk). This is a survival from the early days of geology, before the study of fossils and other reliable indicators had enabled more precise recognition of the comparative age of beds. But it should be noticed that the basis of subdivision of the geological succession now is not lithology, but age; thus i^2 relates to deposits formed early, but not earliest, in the Eocene period, whether they are clays, as at Reading, or pebble beds, as at Blackheath and Woolwich. The legend, however, indicates the lithology of the ' horizon ' over the area shown on the map, whether constant or variable.

The ultimate test of the age of rocks is the order of superposition, for it is obvious that, except in cases of disturbance so violent as to cause inversion, newer rocks rest on older. This applies universally to the sedimentary rocks, by far the most numerous and important group, but for igneous rocks different criteria apply which will be considered later.

Deposition and Erosion

The sementary rocks may be regarded as occurring in layers, not necessarily uniform in thickness, resting one on top of the other. The vast majority have been formed as deposits on the sea floor and are therefore likely to present uniform characters over considerable distances; a few (e.g. the Millstone Grit and some parts of the Old Red Sandstone) have been formed in fresh water or under estuarine and deltaic conditions, others (e.g. some of the Triassic 'New Red Sand-stone') on dry land as desert sands, and these are likely to vary rapidly in composition and thickness from place to place. Still others more limited in area and frequency, have been formed in rivers (terraces and alluvium) or by glaciers and ice-sheets (boulder clay) and their dis-tribution is very patchy and irregular. Such 'superficial' deposits, laid down in the great Ice Age or more recently, are collectively known as 'drift' and are not shown on the 'solid' edition, from which they are imagined to be stripped off, exposing the 'solid' rocks.

Now at any moment of time in geological history marine deposits are being laid down somewhere, while in other areas, above the sea, denudation is occurring and existing beds are being destroyed. And in any locality the geological history will have consisted at one time, of deposition and at another of denudation. This alternation of building up and wearing down forms the basis of the subdivision of geological time; the great formations were laid down during periods of predominant deposition and are separated from each other by periods of predomin-ant erosion when considerable thicknesses of rock were stripped from the surface, so that when, at some later period, the area sank beneath the sea, new rocks were laid down on and across the denuded edges of the older series. Such a relationship is known as an 'unconformity' and major unconformities usually, though not universally, mark the divi-sions between the great eras. It is fortunate for us in Britain that the subdivision and nomenclature of the geological record was in the main the work of British pioneers in the science and is particularly applicable to this country. A few names, such as Permian (Perm, Russia) and Jurassic (Jura Mts.) are a concession to better development of rocks of that age elsewhere, and terms such as Triassic imply a threefold divi-sion which does not apply in these islands. But the major subdivisions conform with the British succession and are less readily applicable, for example, in India or Africa.

It must not, however, be supposed that unconformities do not occur within the formations, they do frequently and importantly, but they are not so widespread or so striking. The changes that converted an area from one of deposition to one of erosion were generally brought about by earth movements so that the rocks below the unconformity were frequently disturbed prior to erosion and there is an angular unconformity, i.e. a discordance of dip and strike between old and new rocks.

Dip and Strike

These terms are defined in text-books of Geology and Physical Geography; but a word of explanation may be desirable here. The layers of rock, when deposited, lie virtually horizontal and the surface at each stage in deposition is known as a bedding plane. Such planes are usually clearly recognizable in the rocks seen in a cliff or quarry even if there is no difference in composition or texture between adjacent layers. Usually the rock has a tendency, often very marked, to split into layers along them. Most rocks, however, have undergone, since deposition, some tilting or folding, so that the bedding planes no longer lie horizontal but have an inclination or 'dip'. Thus the dip may be defined as the direction of steepest slope on a bedding plane and is the direction in which a drop of water would flow if spilt on to an exposed bedding plane. It is expressed on the map by an arrow, with the angle of dip in degrees measured from the horizontal written at the point; it should be noted that the arrow refers only to a dip actually measured in an exposure at the place indicated by the arrow's point and may not be true at a point only a small distance away. Thus a dip is analogous to a hachure line which is drawn down the steepest slope of the land surface, while the dip refers to the steepest slope on a bedding plane, which does not, probably, form the surface of the ground.

The line drawn on any plane at right angles to the steepest slope is necessarily a horizontal line and the direction of such a line, drawn on a bedding plane, is known as the *strike*. Returning to our analogy, a strike line is analogous to a contour, i.e. it joins all points at the same height above sea level, but it relates solely to the bedding plane and has nothing to do with the form of the land. This is a simple and elementary point, but experience has shown that confusion often arises with beginners by failure to restrict the terms 'dip' and 'strike' to the bedding of the rocks and to distinguish them from any necessary connexion with the form of the land. On this analogy, and to emphasize the distinction of connotation, a strike line can be called a 'stratum-contour'.

Determination of Dip from the Map

Provided that the dip undergoes no change within the area considered, it is possible to determine the strike by locating two or more points where the trace of the boundary line of two adjacent strata (i.e. the plane of the top bedding plane of the lower bed) cuts the same contour, i.e. A, B, C and D in Fig. 1, since these points are on the same bedding plane and at the same height above sea level (400 ft.) they lie on the same strike.

The dip is at right angles to this line and must be to the SSW. because the bed outcrops on the spur at E, higher than the strike line and the bedding plane must decline from E to G. Similarly the outcrop at F in the valley bottom (c. 350 ft.) is below the stratum-contour and the bed must decline from H to F.

In practice this can seldom be done precisely, partly because the strike undergoes slight changes, but chiefly because of the limitations of accuracy in mapping the outcrops. We shall return to the practical uses of this method and of its variant (the three-point method) later (p. 21), but at this point it is worth noting that in areas where the dip remains fairly constant it is possible to determine its direction and angle by 'contouring' a given plane with stratum-contours. For example, the outcrop of the thin chalk rock (Fig. 2) is so narrow as to be almost a line. It runs in zigzags along the fretted edge of the chalk escarpment on the Aylesbury Sheet (238) and in deep salients up the valleys that dissect the long dip slope, crossing and recrossing each contour as the rock declines (dips) towards the south-east. By marking each point at which it crosses a contour and joining those points at the same height we have contoured the surface of the chalk rock and determined its direction and amount of dip (south-eastwards at 55 ft. per mile).

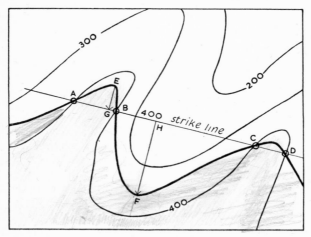

FIG. 1.—Determination of dip from relation of outcrop to contours

Ex.[1] Not many maps are suitable for this exercise for it is rare to find a combination of the favourable circumstances, viz. (1) an unchanging dip, (2) frequent outcrops over a considerable area. Long dip slopes dissected by rivers, such as characterize the Mesozoic beds on the English scarplands, are best, e.g. Witney (236), Kettering (171), Cirencester (235), Henley-on-Thames (254).

A similar method may be used for reconstructing gravel covered erosion surfaces such as terraces.

Ex. Reading sheet (269) drift edition.

Contour the base of the 'Plateau gravels'.

Draw a profile (see p. 29) along the steepest direction of fall. Draw beneath it the profile of the River Kennet and compare the two.

[1] *Ex.* Stands for Exercise or Example or both.

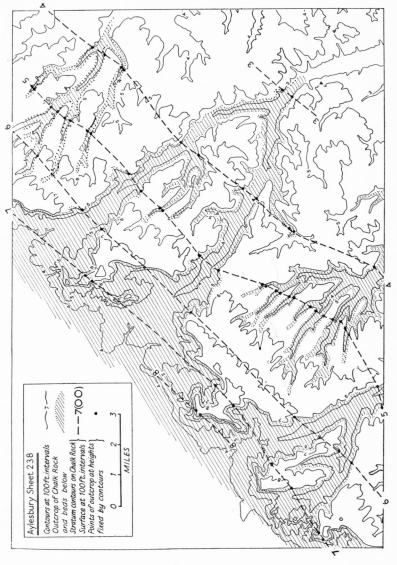

Aylesbury Sheet 238

Contours at 100ft. intervals ————— 7 —

Outcrop of Chalk Rock
and beds below

Stratum contours on Chalk Rock

Surface at 100ft. intervals ——— 7(OO)

Points of outcrop at heights
fixed by contours   •

0   1   2   3
MILES

FIG. 2.—Stratum contours on the 'Chalk Rock'. Aylesbury sheet

Use of Underground Information

To the evidence of dip provided by the altitude of the outcrop can be added that provided from the records of mines, wells, and borings. The memoirs of the Geological Survey (Water Supply, Thicknesses of Strata, &c) provide the raw material for such exercises, but a much wider search for information is generally necessary if a full and reliable map is to be constructed. An example of a map constructed in this way is that of 'Post-Alpine relief of SE. England as indicated by the contours of the sub-Eocene surface'.[1]

Thickness of Strata

The diagram (Fig. 3) shows that the calculation of thickness from measured width of outcrop (on flat land) and the angle of dip is a simple problem of triangles; for b (thickness) $= a$ (width of outcrop) $\times \cos \theta$ (angle of dip). And c (thickness to be passed through in a vertical boring) $= a \times \cot \theta$.

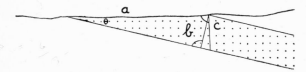

FIG. 3.—Simple geometry of dip, thickness, and outcrop width

All problems of dip, strike, and outcrop are capable of a mathematical solution (see K. W. Earle).[2]

Form and Breadth of Outcrop

The area over which a bed of rock comes to the surface of the ground is known as its *outcrop*, but the rock itself may be exposed only occasionally, if at all, over this area, being generally hidden by a mantle of rock waste and soil. The area of the outcrop is coloured on the map with the appropriate colour and is clearly divided from the outcrop of the next bed by a line (the trace); this line is drawn dotted where the junction of the two rocks is obscured by a cover of drift or is uncertain for any other reason.

The form of the outcrop may be wide or narrow, continuous or discontinuous, and the boundary lines may be straight or curved, regular or irregular, depending on two variable controls—(1) the slope of the ground and (2) the dip of the beds. If, for instance, a given bed appears twice at the surface separated by the outcrop of a younger bed it is clear that either the slope of the ground has changed or the dip of

---

[1] *Structure, Surface and Drainage in South-East England*, Wooldridge and Linton. Institute of British Geographers, Publication No. 10, 1939, Fig. 5.

[2] Kenneth W. Earle, *Dip and Strike problems mathematically surveyed*, London, 1934.

the rock has changed, or both; which of the two is responsible in an actual case can be verified by an examination of the relief and the dip arrows. The arrangement may have been brought about by (1) a ridge of high ground carved out of horizontal strata (Fig. 4a) or (2) a syncline eroded to a flat surface (4b) or (3) both arrangements in combination

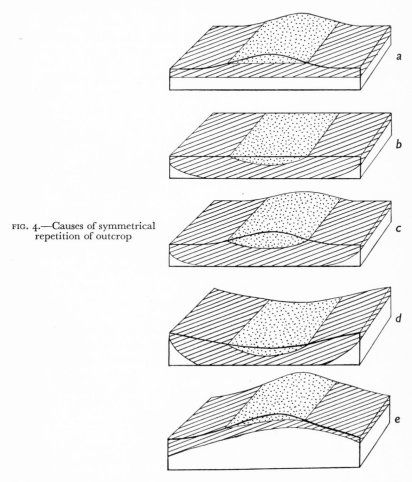

FIG. 4.—Causes of symmetrical repetition of outcrop

(4c). But it can be seen from the figure that the arrangement can further be produced by (4) a valley with slopes less steep than the dips of the syncline (4d) and (5) a hill with slopes steeper than the dips of the anticline (4e); i.e. it is the relative inclination of the strata (dip) and of the ground (slope) that determines outcrop. The limiting cases of width of outcrop are: (1) slope of ground parallel to dip: the same bed outcrops over the whole surface where this relationship holds. (Fig. 5*a*); (2) slope of ground perpendicular to dip; the width of outcrop on the ground is the same as the thickness of the bed (bed 2 on Fig. 5*b*).   But note that it will not be the same *on the map* except in the limiting case of vertical beds outcropping on horizontal ground, though the difference will not be great except on very steep slopes; outcrops on a vertical cliff face cannot be shown at all on a map.   Between these two extreme cases are all gradations, the width of outcrop (for a bed of given thickness) increasing as the angle between dip and slope increases (cf. beds 2 and 3 on Fig. 5).

In considering the relationship between outcrop and relief it is convenient to consider the 'trace' (outcrop of a junction plane between

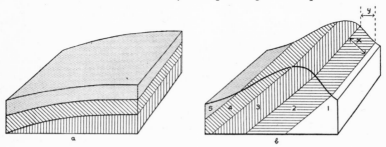

FIG. 5.—Limiting cases of width of outcrop
x = width on ground: *y* = width on map

two strata) rather than the total width of outcrop of a bed, because the junction plane has no width and is a plane in the geometrical sense; its outcrop will be the intersection of this plane with the surface of the ground whose form is shown by the contours. It is obvious that the outcrops of horizontal beds will follow faithfully the contour lines, since both represent the intersection of horizontal planes with the ground, and that the outcrops of vertical beds will cut across the map in straight lines independent of contours since a map is viewed vertically. As the dip steepens, so the outcrops become less and less parallel to the contours and more and more independent of them.

Development of Outcrop from a Measured Dip

Provided that the dip of a bed is known and remains constant in direction and amount, it is always possible to plot in the outcrop on a map by a simple geometrical construction which is much used in the geological mapping of an area where exposures are few. In Fig. 6 let us suppose that the lower surface of, say, a bed of limestone 100 ft. thick is observed to outcrop at *A* with a dip of 5° in the direction of the arrow. Now *A* is on the 500-ft. contour, so that the base of the limestone is here at 500 ft. above sea level. A line drawn through this point at right angles to the dip will be a stratum-contour and along this line the base of the bed is everywhere at 500 ft. Clearly, therefore, wherever this line crosses the 500-ft. surface contour the bed of rock must be at the surface of the ground, i.e. it outcrops. This happens at *B*, *C* and *D*. Now the contour interval of our map gives us precise information about the height of land at each 100 ft., so the next step is to 'contour' the base of the bed so that we may apply at each contour the method we have applied to the 500-ft. contour. Now the

cotangent of 5° is 11·45 $\left(\text{i.e. } \dfrac{\text{Base}}{\text{Perpendicular}} = 11·45\right)$; but the perpendicular is to be 100 ft, so the base will be 100 × 11·43 = 1,143 ft.,

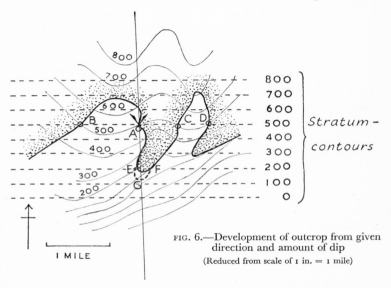

FIG. 6.—Development of outcrop from given direction and amount of dip

(Reduced from scale of 1 in. = 1 mile)

1 MILE

i.e. the horizontal distance between strike lines at 100-ft. interval is to be 1,143 ft. But the scale of the map is 1/63,360 or 1 in. = 5,280 ft., therefore the horizontal distance on the map will be $\dfrac{1,143 \text{ ft.}}{5,280} = 0·22$ in.

N.B. Alternatively the triangle (perpendicular 100 ft., dip 5) can be drawn to scale and the base measured.

Now prolong the dip line across the map and step off on it distances of 0·22 in. and through them draw lines at right angles to the dip, i.e. parallel to the strike. These are stratum-contours at 100-ft. vertical intervals and can be numbered accordingly. Now every point where a contour is cut by a stratum-contour of the same altitude is a point on the outcrop and can be marked with a ⊙. Join these up *intelligently* and the outcrop is developed. In joining up it is essential that no contour or stratum-contour should be crossed until the marked point is reached. For instance in joining E and F the line must be taken as shown by the full line and not by the dotted line which crosses the 200 ft. contour at G. A moment's reflection will show that this point cannot be on the outcrop, for the ground is at 200 ft. but the rock surface is about halfway between 100 and 200 ft. and must be about 50 ft. below ground.

In a similar way we may 'contour' the upper surface of the bed if we know how thick it is. For simplicity we have taken a thickness of 100 ft. so that all that is necessary is to re-number the stratum-contours 100 ft. *lower* and follow the same procedure, marking the points of outcrop x and joining up. Notice that this is not quite accurate because since the bed has a dip of 5° the vertical distance between top and bottom (AB) (c.f. Fig. 3, p. 17) is not quite the same as the thickness (AC). But with low angles of dip the error is not significant, though with steeper angles the length of the vertical must be calculated from the sine of the angle.

Three-point Maps

In applying the method as used in the foregoing exercise quite serious errors may be introduced by a slightly inaccurate measurement of dip, and it must be borne in mind that the precise measurement of dip in one exposure is not easy. Greater accuracy can therefore be attained if the altitude of the plane of the rock surface can be checked over a wide area and this is the form in which the problem is usually presented. Any three points, not in the same straight line, determine the form of a plane, so that if we are told the altitude of the plane at three points we have all the necessary data—hence the name 'three-point method'.

In the map shown in Fig. 7 the surface of the bed of rock is exposed at A and B and is encountered in a well-boring at C on the 400-ft. contour, 100 ft. below the ground (i.e. at 300 O.D.). Join the points A, B, and C. Along the line AB the rock falls from 800 ft. to 600 ft. and at a point halfway along this line the bed is at 700 ft. Along the line AC the bed falls from 800 ft. to 300 ft. (500 ft). Divide this line into 5 equal parts each of which represents a fall of 100 ft. Along BC the bed falls from 600 ft. to 300 ft. (300 ft.). Divide this line into 3 equal parts. Lines joining the points thus determined will be stratum-contours and will be found, of course, to be parallel and equally spaced provided the dip remains unchanged. Further stratum-contours, above the highest point and below the lowest point determined, may be drawn parallel and equally spaced. The remainder of the exercise is similar to the previous one.

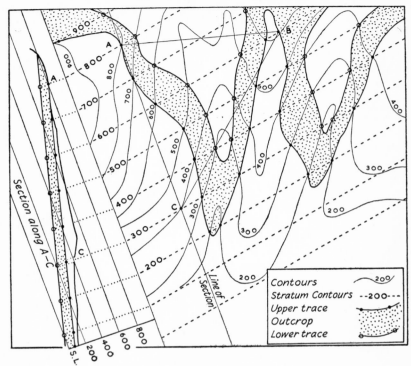

FIG. 7.—Three-point method of developing outcrop

Outcrops on Spurs and in Valleys

Ex. A few exercises of this type, which the student should devise and execute for himself, will soon demonstrate the following points about outcrops on spurs and in valleys which will be found very useful in deducing the direction and amount of dip when these are not actually given on the map.

A. Beds dipping downstream in valleys:

    (1) More steeply than the thalweg. Outcrops tongue downstream.

    (2) Less steeply than the thalweg. Outcrops tongue upstream.

    (3) At same angle as thalweg slope. Parallel outcrops down valley sides; but this arrangement rarely survives over long distances.

B. Beds dipping upstream in valleys:

    Outcrop always tongues upstream. Note that the outcrop in this case passes from high contours on sides to low contours in valley floor. Contrast the case A2 where the outcrop passes from low contours on

sides to higher contours in valley floor. On spurs the opposite relationship holds good. It also follows that the boundary lines of outcrops of
strata dipping into a hillside are less winding than the contours, while
those dipping downhill are more winding. This is shown diagrammatically in Fig. 8.

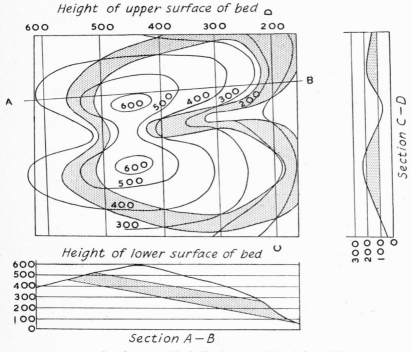

FIG. 8.—Outcrop of bed, dipping into hill and downhill

Types of Outcrop Associated with Different Structures

Certain structures give rise to patterns of outcrop that can be
recognized at a glance. With a little imagination all of them can be
visualized as intersections of two planes, the bedding planes of the
rocks and the more irregular and undulating surface of the ground;
the student should acquire by practice the power of 'seeing solid', of
visualizing the relationship between plan and section.

Ex. The best way to learn the relationship of the outcrop (map)
and structure (section) is to construct for one's self block diagrams (like
that in Figs. 9 and 10) of simple structures such as the following. (The
numbers and titles of geological maps recommended for displaying the
structures are given where possible.)

3

I. Folding.

1. Dipping strata: Newer strata come on in the direction of dip. 235, Cirencester.
2. Symmetrical anticline: Beds repeated symmetrically in order 3, 2, 1, 2, 3, about the axes of the fold, with the oldest exposed in the axis.
3. Symmetrical syncline: The same but with newest exposed in the axis; order 1, 2, 3, 2, 1. 267, Hungerford.
4. Asymmetrical folds: Repetition of beds, but width of outcrop wider where dip is gentle and narrower where it is steep. 285, Aldershot, special sheet Isle of Wight.
5. Overfolds. Repetition of beds but with the dip apparently always in the same direction.

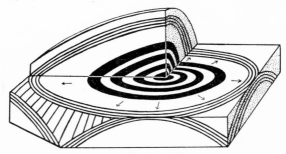

FIG. 9.—Sectional dome

6. Pitching folds. Note the outcrops in pitching anticlines close in the direction of pitch and synclines open in this direction. 123, Stoke on Trent.
7. Domes. These may be regarded as anticlines pitching in both directions away from a central axis, if oval, or central point, if circular (Fig. 9). 112, Chesterfield, S.E. England on ¼-in. scale.
8. Basins. Double case of pitching syncline. Scotland 32, Edinburgh.

II. Strike Faults (i.e. line of fault parallel to strike). 121, Wrexham; 235, Cirencester; 18, Brampton; 112, Chesterfield, and many others.

9. Normal faults. (Hade to downthrow side.)
   a. Hade opposite to dip; beds repeated in order 1, 2, 3, 1, 2, 3.
   b. Hade with dip but steeper; beds cut out at surface.
   c. Hade with dip but less steep (rare); beds repeated.

10. Reversed faults. (Hade to upthrow side.)
    a. Hade opposite to dip; beds cut out.
    b. Hade with dip but steeper; beds repeated.
    c. Hade with dip but less steep; beds cut out.

N.B. If the throw is small or the beds are thick, the next bed above or below may not be brought to the surface, so that instead of repetition there may be only a widening of the outcrop in which the fault occurs, and instead of omission there may be a narrowing.

III. Dip Faults (direction of fault parallel to dip).
    11. In uniformly dipping strata: Note outcrop is displaced in the direction of the dip on the *upthrow* side; this is a general rule for all dip faults.

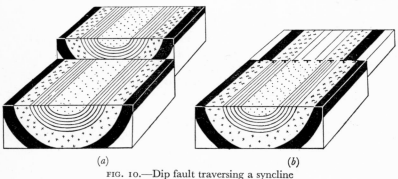

(a)   (b)

FIG. 10.—Dip fault traversing a syncline
(a) uneroded; (b) planed by erosion

12. Faulted anticlines present a double case of the above arrangement. Beds are omitted in the downthrow side or outcrops are brought closer together.
13. Faulted syncline: Beds omitted on upthrow side (Fig. 10).

Note most faults are strictly parallel with neither dip nor strike, but run obliquely, producing, in varying degrees, some of the consequences of each kind.

Unconformity

The origin and significance of unconformity have been mentioned on p. 13. It will be noted that when one series of rocks rests unconformably on another the outcrops of the older series are no longer continuous, but cease at the point where the bed disappears beneath the cover of the unconformable ones.

One bed, the basal bed of the new formation, rests here on one bed of the older formation, there on another; in fact the easiest way to detect an unconformity from the map is by the coming together at one point (*A* on Fig. 11) of three formations, two of the older series and one (the basal one) of the newer. This can never happen with conformable strata except (*a*) by faulting, (*b*) a vertical cliff.

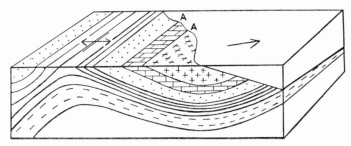

FIG. 11.—Unconformity

Good examples of unconformity are seen on the following sheets: Brampton (18), Chesterfield (112), Wrexham (121), Cardiff (263). On the Cardiff sheet the Trias is seen to rest on a 'hilly' surface carved out of Silurian, Devonian, and Carboniferous strata folded into long anticlines and synclines (see Fig. 14).

Overlap

When the sea is encroaching further and further on to a shore plain, beds laid down late in the succession will be deposited resting directly on the old land surface, overlapping those laid down during the early stages of the encroachment. Such a process is naturally nearly always accompanied by unconformity since the land area over which

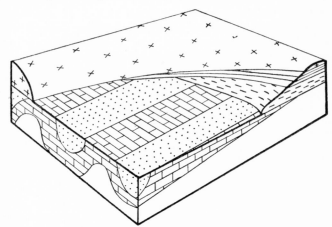

FIG. 12.—Unconformity with overlap

the new sea advances will necessarily have undergone denudation during the land episode. Again the easiest way to recognize such an arrangement is by the coming together of three strata at a point, but in this case the outcrop of one of the *old* series is in contact with two of the *newer* (overlapping) series (Fig. 12). For example, south of London the Thanet sands are overlapped by the Woolwich and Reading beds which come to rest direct on the chalk. Examples of unconformity with overlap can be seen on sheets: Devizes (282), Bridport (327), Aldershot (285).

Section II. Examination by Sections

Section Drawing

This is more than an exercise, it is a practice essential to the understanding of structure. When experience has been gained the structure may be appreciated from careful inspection of the map but not with the degree of precision and accuracy that is often required. The function of the section is to explain and illustrate the geological structure, and the choice of the most suitable line or lines for this purpose is a matter of some importance. The most revealing direction, generally speaking, is the direction of dip, for this will show the true dip and will probably traverse the maximum number of formations. If unconformities are present the line of section should be chosen in such a way as to reveal their nature clearly, and as the dip of the strata below and above the plane of unconformity probably differs, this may involve some compromise of the principle enunciated above. But in any case the strike section must be avoided as giving a false impression of horizontal beds. The direction of dip may vary over a map, even without unconformity, and the student need not be afraid of drawing a section along two or more lines meeting at obtuse angles, but in this case the change of direction must be clearly indicated on the section.

A section is supplied on the bottom of nearly all 1 in. geological maps and the line of this section is indicated on the map itself. This is usually cut off for teaching and examination purposes, but the line may generally be adopted by the student for his own section as it will have been selected with care by the Geological Survey in the first case. In all cases the line selected for the section must be clearly indicated on the section; the compass directions should be written at each end and the position of easily identifiable towns, hills, rivers, &c. should be marked by perpendicular lines rising from the section with the name written at the top. The next problem that presents itself is the choice of a suitable vertical scale. If the map is on the 1 in. scale, as it usually will be, it is necessary to exaggerate the vertical scale, for even Ben Nevis, drawn to true scale, is less than 1 in. high. When the vertical scale has been exaggerated (perhaps $\frac{1}{10}$ in. = 100 ft.) all dips and slopes are gravely distorted and a very false impression is produced. For example if the vertical scale is exaggerated five times a dip of 11° (1 in 5) will appear as 45° (1 in 1). More serious than this is the distortion of thickness that inevitably results. For example a bed of rock 500 ft. thick will, if horizontal, have its thickness shown in accordance with the vertical scale ($\frac{1}{2}$ in., if the vertical scale is 1 in. = 1,000 ft.); but if, vertical, its thickness will be shown in accordance with the horizontal

28

scale ($\frac{1}{10}$ in. on the 1 in. scale). Beds dipping at intermediate angles will have intermediate exaggeration of thicknesses on the section. Thus in a monoclinal fold a section so drawn would present a grossly erroneous appearance of considerable thinning out as each bed turned over towards the vertical. The Isle of Wight (special sheet) is a good example. In practice this misleading result of the use of two scales is 'adjusted' to give a more natural impression, but inaccuracy is the price to be paid. It is therefore preferable, though not always feasable, for the beginner to use the 6 in. scale, on which, by the use of great care and a very sharp pencil, a natural scale can be used and true dips and slopes reproduced.

But supposing that a section is to be drawn across a 1 in. map, the first general principle to be adopted in the selection of the vertical scale is that it should be as small as possible, consistent with the clear representation of the structure, so that distortion may be reduced to a minimum. In general a section about 1 in. high is convenient, but a larger scale may have to be adopted if numerous strata with low dips and small thicknesses have to be shown. Conversely if the strata are thick and have high dips a smaller scale may be used. Graph paper ruled in tenths of an inch, and preferably the kind without thickening of the 1-in. squares should always be used. Plain drawing paper should not be used because (1) the altitude lines can never be drawn accurately or neatly enough with ruler and pencil or ink and (2) the vertical ruling is required for the accurate transfer of altitudes, outcrops, &c. from the edge of the paper where they are marked off to the line of section.

The topographic section (profile) can now be drawn in the usual way by placing the upper or, if preferred, the lower edge of the graph paper along the line of section, marking off the point at which each contour cuts the line of section and projecting this point down to its appropriate altitude line. The topographic section should be put in lightly in pencil, for it will probably have to be modified as work progresses to fit in the outcrops satisfactorily. Remember that the slopes that have been drawn in between the points fixed by contours are not known but are based on guesswork even if you have been guided by spot heights and the hachuring which is present on some geological maps.

Next comes the geology. Each outcrop must be marked in on the top (or bottom) of the paper strip and transferred vertically to the ground profile of the section. In practice it is better to deal with the boundary lines (traces) between the top of the bed and the bottom of the next rather than with the whole width of the coloured outcrop, for the former are planes in the geometrical sense, without thickness, the latter are not.

If we take one of these traces which occurs frequently over the map and plot it in all along the section we shall get a general idea of the structure at an early stage, which will simplify the later progress. The beds must be fitted in to outcrop in their proper places without violating any information on the map, dips must be consistent with those shown and relief must be consistent with the contour lines. There are many alternative incorrect solutions, all of which involve contradictions, but there is one, and only one, correct one which is fully satisfactory.

It will often be found necessary to examine the ground on either side of the section in order to obtain information as to dips, &c., but it must be remembered that dip arrows refer only to the dip at the point represented by the tip of the arrow, and the legitimacy must always be weighed of extending such information to the line of section. Often also the interpretation of the section itself is ambiguous or even impossible without taking into consideration the information supplied by the bordering land, e.g. in cases where the underlying rocks are hidden under an unconformable cover (see below).

Faults (see p. 24)

The hade of a fault may be estimated from the behaviour of the fault plane on spurs and valleys, which is, of course, subject to the same rules as those governing the behaviour of bedding planes (see p. 22). But since the hade is often nearly vertical the line of the fault may be almost independent of relief. The downthrow side of a fault is usually marked on the map by a small line projecting from the fault line thus ———,——— but, in any case, it can usually be deduced by its effect on outcrop, newer rocks being found on the downthrow side.

Unconformity (see p. 25 and fig. 13)

This will probably have been recognized by inspection before section drawing is begun; if not it will soon intrude itself on the notice. As soon as this happens it is advisable to select the basal plane of the overlying series and plot it in over the whole section. Proceed then with all the overlying series and return finally to the 'basement' series below the unconformity. Where these are hidden by the unconformable series these outcrops should be continued to the points at which they would have met the line of section and these points should be transferred, not to the surface of the ground but to the base of the unconformity. Thus the boundary between 3 and 4 that passes beneath 6 at the point *A* would meet the line of section at *B* and is transferred to the section at *C*. Similarly the boundary between 4 and 5, concealed beneath the patch of 6 on the hill-top, crosses the section line at *D* and is transferred to the section at *E*. This patch separated from the main outcrop of 6 by erosion is known as an 'outlier'. It provides a clue to the former extension of the bed 6.

The plane of unconformity is not necessarily a flat one, though the abrading action of the sea that accompanies the new submergence generally produces a fairly flat plane of marine abrasion. But the plane of marine abrasion may have undergone warping or deformation

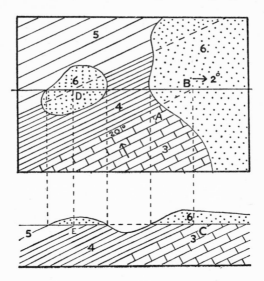

FIG. 13.—Unconformity: map and section

subsequent to its formation and burial. Furthermore islands or 'sea-stacks' may survive the attack of the waves and will be buried bit by bit beneath the new deposits. Surfaces produced by sub-aerial erosion,

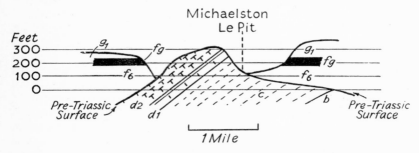

FIG. 14.—Unconformity on undulating surface

whether in humid or in arid climates, may be much more irregular, e.g. the desert landscape buried under and partially exhumed from the Trias in Charnwood Forest. A good example, already referred to on p. 26, is seen on the Cardiff sheet (fig. 14).

Overlap (see p. 26).

Circumstances such as those just described, if on a considerable scale, give rise to overlap, later and later beds coming to rest on the sloping surface of unconformity as the sea gradually encroaches on to the old land. In drawing the section the same principles should guide us as when dealing with unconformity. Fig. 15 is based on the Marl-

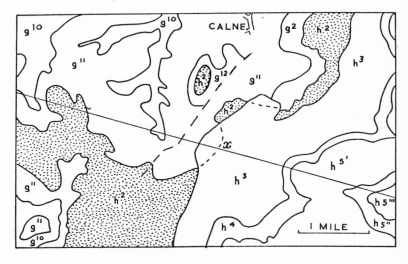

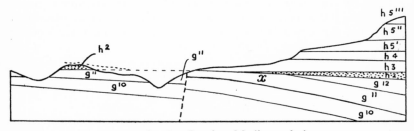

FIG. 15.—Overlap. Based on Marlborough sheet

borough sheet (266). h^2 does not appear at the surface in the centre of the map on the line of section, where there was probably a slight prominence in the old floor: it is therefore overlapped by h^3 which rests directly on g^{11}, but it occurs on either side of the line of section where there were probably embayments; it may justifiably, from the evidence of the map, be assumed to exist beneath h^3 on the line of the section, its reconstructed limits being represented by the dotted line which cuts the section at x; east of this point a wedge of h^2 must be inserted on the section.

Determination of the Age of Structures

The simple rule, based on common sense, is that folds and faults are later than the latest beds they affect and earlier than the earliest beds that they do not affect. But sometimes movement along a line of fold or fault may occur at intervals, being renewed at a later date after a period of quiescence. Thus an older series of rocks may be profoundly disturbed, while a newer series, resting unconformably on them, may be disturbed along similar trend lines, though less violently. For example the Cretaceous sediments of South-eastern England, in the Weald and the London Basin, are bent into anticlines and synclines running in general from west to east, but the dips, except locally in the Isle of Wight and the Hog's Back, are of a low order. These folds date from the Alpine orogeny of Mid-Tertiary time. But beneath them lie, at great depth, Palaeozoic sediments folded in the same direction but much more severely in the Hercynian orogeny of late Carboniferous times. These latter are a continuation of the steeply dipping folds of the Mendips and South Wales and are met, under the Cretaceous cover, in a number of deep borings from Wiltshire to the Dover Coalfield.

When sediments are both folded and faulted the two kinds of movement may be contemporary and due to the same earth movements. In this case their trends will be related and must be capable of a single explanation by pressure in one direction. More usually, however, the faults are later than the folds and displace them. For sediments, once folded, acquire a certain rigidity which makes them prone to fracture when pressure is applied at a later date.

When two or more sets of faults occur in one region they may be contemporary, but more usually one set, characterized by a parallelism of trend, is later than another, with a different trend. One set will displace the other and is manifestly newer in age. There may be as many as three 'families' of faults each with a distinct trend and of separate ages. But renewal of movement along old established lines must always be envisaged as a possibility.

Ex. Fig. 16, which is an invention, contains certain errors and contradictions which the student may detect by drawing sections from *A* to *B*, *C* to *D*, *E* to *F*, or in any other direction which, it is thought, might reveal the structure. If he can spot the deliberate mistakes without resort to section drawing he has made very good progress and is endowed with unusually good visual perception. It is an excellent test at this stage to invent some geological maps for oneself and to check whether they are possible.

Ex. Fig 17 represents a skeleton map containing information determined by a field geologist from scattered exposures. Complete the map. The solution is given in fig. 67.

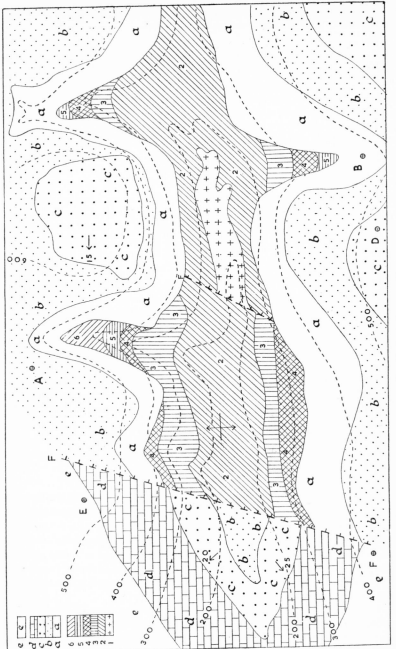

FIG. 16.—Geological map with errors

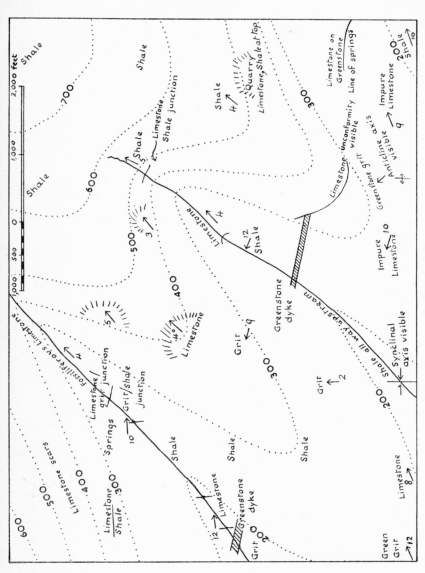

FIG. 17.—Geologist's field map

Igneous Rocks

Hitherto we have concerned ourselves with sedimentary rocks, which, occuring in layers, are subject to certain simple geometrical rules in the relation of outcrop to dip and slope. But igneous rocks, whose mode of occurrence is fundamentally different, require separate treatment. Some lava flows, ashes and intrusive sills occur in layers resembling sedimentary strata but their lateral extension is generally much less and their thickness much less uniform. Other types, intruded from below, take the form of laccoliths, phacolites, dykes, plugs, &c. On their mode of occurrence will depend the manner in which they are shown in the section and much help can be derived from the legend, which always states the nature of rocks and whether they are contemporaneous or intrusive.

Broadly speaking the contemporaneous groups, lava flows, ashes, and agglomerates occur as irregular layers or lenticles, while the intrusive may be divided into (1) large intrusive masses like laccolites, (2) small wall-like dykes, (3) cylindrical plugs, (4) sills sometimes thickening into phacolites. The last are intruded in a horizontal direction and tend to follow bedding planes, though often transgressing from one horizon to another. The first three are intruded across the bedding planes and may be shown as passing downwards to the bottom of the section.

Much information about the mode of occurrence can be derived from the study of the outcrop in relation to the relief.

Fig. 18, based on the Penzance Sheet (351), shows several types of igneous rocks in map and section. Other informative sheets for the study of igneous rocks are: Ben Nevis (Scot. 53), The Cheviot (5), Brampton (18), Falmouth (352), Dartmoor (338).

The Age of Igneous Rocks

Extrusive rocks are younger than the youngest sediments they rest on and older than the oldest sediments that rest on them. Intrusive rocks are younger than the youngest rocks into which they are intruded, but older than the oldest they fail to intrude: they may often be observed to end abruptly against the edge of the outcrop of some series which is apparently burying their former extension.

Where two or more types of igneous rocks are seen in juxtaposition their relative ages can be determined on principles listed above. As a rule it will be observed that the minor intrusions (dykes and sills) penetrate lava flows and the larger (plutonic) intrusions. This is because they are generally intruded in the late stages of the volcanic cycle.

The test of included fragments cannot be applied in map work, but valuable information as to the age of identifiable igneous (and sedimentary) rocks is often provided by their occurence as pebbles or

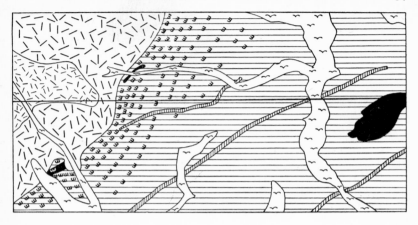

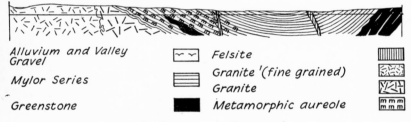

Alluvium and Valley
Gravel

Mylor Series

Greenstone

Felsite

Granite '(fine grained)
Granite

Metamorphic aureole

FIG. 18.—Igneous rocks. Penzance sheet

mineral fragments in other rocks, which must, of course, be later in age than the exposure of the parent material.

Ex. Determine the relative ages of the igneous rocks shown in Fig. 19.

Drift Deposits

These, which are always 'unconformable' on the solid rock, should be put in last, as patches wherever they occur. They should be given as far as possible their correct form, alluvium filling valleys, gravels and clay-with-flints, if occurring on chalk, piped into it to some extent, &c.

The whole section should be made of sufficient depth to show clearly the underground structure and may be carried, if necessary, below sea level, but it should not be taken to depths where the structure is hypothetical and indeterminable from the evidence on the map. Finally, sections should be finished in Indian ink for neatness and coloured or shaded for clarity. Ideally the colours used on the map for

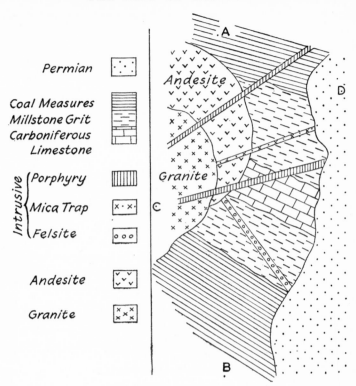

Permian

Coal Measures
Millstone Grit
Carboniferous
Limestone

Intrusive {
Porphyry

Mica Trap

Felsite
}

Andesite

Granite

FIG. 19.—Relative age of igneous rocks

each formation should be imitated as closely as possible in the section and a thin wash of this colour used for the appropriate formation. But if paints or coloured inks are not available a clear system of shading should be used following the conventional methods of representation for each rock type, fine lines for shaly rocks, dots for sandstones, 'bricks' for limestones, &c. In any case the index letters and figures of the formation should be written on each bed where space permits.

Interpretation of Geological Maps

Properly interpreted the geological map is a mine of valuable information to the physiographer; in fact the relief of a region cannot be properly understood or explained without a knowledge of the geology. The influence of geology on water supply, mineral wealth, industry, agriculture, settlement, and human activities generally, though all vital to the geographer, are beyond the scope of this book, but because structure is one of the major determinants of relief a full understanding of all that geological structure implies is essential.

Geological History

Stage by stage the episodes in the geological history of an area can be read off from a map. We can, of course, only take the story back to the time of the oldest deposits shown on the map, and their nature gives us a clue to the conditions obtaining over the area at the time of their deposition. If these are marine deposits their texture and composition tell us something of the depth of water and the distance from land; or they may be fresh water, estuarine, desert, or even glacial in origin.

We must next determine whether the structure is simple or complex, i.e. whether there have been one, two, or more geological cycles with intervening periods of deformation and denudation. To do this we study first the legend and find whether any formations or parts of formations are missing. If so then there is a definite break in the continuity of geological history, which is certain to be marked by an unconformity on the map. Often this hiatus is indicated in the legend by a sloping or uneven line at the top of the column where the break occurs.

The first beds shown in the column above the break indicate the time at which deposition was resumed and often this will be a basal conglomerate marking the return of the sea, We now turn to the map and study the structure of the 'basement', i.e. the oldest, pre-unconformity series, and note the nature and trend of the folding and faulting, from which we reconstruct what happened to it during the missing interval for which no sediments occur. Our next operation is to analyse the nature of the surface of the unconformable junction. It may be a smooth plane of marine abrasion like the base of the Eocene where it rests on the chalk, or it may be a highly irregular and hilly topography like the pre-Triassic surface in the Midlands, e.g. Charnwood Forest. Such a surface, indurated during the long interval of geological time, may be partially stripped of its cover of sediments and re-exposed as a fossil plane exerting a powerful influence on topography, e.g. the stripped sub-Eocene surface on the Chiltern Hills (see p. 64).

The duration of the interval of erosion is not a simple matter to estimate. The mere absence of rocks of a certain age is not evidence of erosional conditions at that time; they may have been deposited and subsequently removed. All we can say with certainty is that at some time after the period represented by the newest surviving beds (and the whole map must be searched for these) erosion began. But we can be certain of the date of the recommencement of deposition. The characteristics of these new deposits must be examined and overlap looked for; if detected the direction of overlap gives the direction of sea and land at the time.

Next we go through the same routine of examination that was applied to the basement and apply it to the newer cover rocks, examining first the conditions of deposition and then of deformation, remembering that any deformation it has undergone has necessarily been

4

imposed on the basement series. If, for example, a Cretaceous cover has a dip to the east of 5°, then 5° must be subtracted from all eastward dips and added to all westward dips of the basement in assessing the pre-Cretaceous structure.

Geology and Relief

Except in extreme youth in the geographical cycle, before differential erosion has had time to produce contrasts of relief, and again in extreme old age, as represented by the peneplain, when the influence of structure is virtually effaced, the contrasts in resistance to erosion will inevitably cause the softer beds to be worn down more rapidly than the harder. Therefore in the vast majority of landscapes in which contrasted rock types are represented the height of the land is a reflection of the competence or powers of resistance of the various beds. In general, therefore, highland and lowland are directly related to lithology, and if there are exceptions to this rule then some other reason must be sought, e.g. recent uplift or protection by a resistant cover now destroyed.

It is impossible to lay down universal rules of relative competence of rocks to resist erosion, because there are considerable variations of composition and texture in each type, and because other influences, such as climate and erosional process, modify their powers of resistance, but the general behaviour of the commoner types is stated below. The arrangement is in approximately decreasing order of resistance.

Quartzite

Very resistant. Bedded rocks, but generally ancient and characteristic of areas of intense disturbance. Therefore generally with high dips and forming ridges. Uniformity of texture, great hardness, and absence of jointing produce continuous, not stepped, slopes and conical forms.

Gneiss

Very resistant, massive, and often of great thickness. Forms uplands with generally rounded forms except under frost action. Very ancient, so often much reduced by erosion.

Granite

Rather similar to gneiss, but exfoliates and disintegrates more rapidly in hot and especially in arid climates. The decomposition of felspar, its weakest mineral component, loosens the texture and causes rapid decay in hot, moist climates.

Basalt

Resistant, strongly jointed, often columnar. Occurs as lava flows (often very extensive), sills, or dykes. Therefore usually either plateau, escarpment, or ridge.

Andesite, Rhyolite, &c.

Resistant. Dykes and sills and lava flows. Rather similar to basalt, but much less extensive.

Conglomerate

Rather similar to quartzite, especially if well cemented, but the greater weakness of the cement and the variability of composition reduce their resistance. Bedded. Form ridges and escarpments when tilted.

Sandstone and Gravel

Usually strong, but resistance variable depending on porosity and degree of cementation. Varies from loose sand to quartzite. Marked jointing in harder types gives a tendency to produce mesas and cuestas.

Slate

Moderately resistant. Despite characteristic cleavage it makes rounded hill masses.

Limestone

Resistant on account of porosity and joint-system enlarged by solution. Produces dry plateaux and escarpments. But much weaker in wet climates and at altitudes within reach of the water-table because of solubility.

Chalk

Behaviour similar to limestone, but softer and less resistant. Less marked joint system, therefore more rounded forms. Convex profile common.

Shale

Rather weak. Produces lowlands and gentle slopes.

Sand

Weak, but porous. Therefore often forms highlands because of scarcity of surface drainage.

Clay

Weak and soft. Slippery when wet, therefore low angle of rest in wet climates, low relief and gentle slopes. Steeper slopes and bluffs in arid climates.

Marl

Weak. Lowlands and gentle slopes.

It is noteworthy that the igneous rocks all come high in scale of resistance, as do the rocks characteristic of ancient (indurated) formations—gneiss, quartzite, sandstone, and slate. Lowest in the scale come the soft sediments characteristic of the Mesozoic and Tertiary—marls, clays and sands.

The influence of geology on drainage and the evolution of relief should be noted at this stage and also the influence of glaciation, if any, but these problems will be considered in the next chapter dealing with surface morphology. The form of the land can be explained in terms of structure, process, and stage. The tools used in each process, the sea, rivers, glaciers, or wind, leave characteristic and easily recognized marks on the landscape and all are destructive, though in different ways. To identify the tool used (process) and to estimate how far the process has gone (stage) is the work of the geomorphologist, using the form of the land surface as his evidence. So while the geologist is concerned with the building of the crust and with the deposition and deformation of the rocks that are there to be seen, the geomorphologist is concerned with what is no longer there, with the gap that denudation has produced. He attempts to reconstruct the events that have occurred during the hiatus in time from the traces that those events have impressed on the drainage system and the relief.

CHAPTER 3

SURFACE MORPHOLOGY: THE RELIEF MAP

A GOOD topographic map is a document which presents to the eye simultaneously as much information as could be packed, in word form, into a good-sized book; it is therefore quite impossible to absorb all this information at once, and any attempt to do so must result in a state of mental confusion and bewilderment. The information with which the map confronts us is of a miscellaneous nature, physical, human, and economic facts are shown intimately interwoven, but in their true space relationships; in fact by no other medium can the interrelation be so clearly portrayed. The scope of this book is, however, limited to the physical aspects and its object is to show how far, from the map alone, the physiography of a region can be described and its origin deduced; to add the interpretation of the human and economic geography would demand a sequel of at least equal length. With this restricted objective in view the proper way to examine the map is to concentrate on those facts that are relevant, i.e. the methods of representing relief. There are two kinds, statistical and pictorial. Hachures, form-lines and hill shading help to give pictorial representation, but their value for the present purpose is limited by their lack of precision and objectivity. Spot heights and trigonometrical points, on the contrary, are accurately surveyed, and the contours based on them are shown wherever they 'exist'; no selection is exercised over their insertion or omission. These, therefore, give a true representation of height, but unfortunately not a complete one.

The map, having only two dimensions in which to represent three, must relegate the third to a conventional method which cannot show height as a continuous distribution. True height is known along the contours, but between contours it is only known within the limits (perhaps 100 ft.) of the contour interval used. We must never forget that we can only get out of a map what the surveyor and cartographer have put into it. To interpolate, however carefully and discretely it is done, is to go beyond the ascertained facts; all interpolations must be suspect.

But with all its limitations the contour map presents to the eye a great volume of statistical fact about altitude. Much can be learnt from inspection of the map, but when its possibilities by this method have been exhausted there still remains infinitely more that can be extracted by quantitative analysis and rearrangement of the data. It will be assumed here that the possibilities of inspection have been exhausted and that the reader is thoroughly familiar with the commonest contour patterns representing different kinds of valleys and divides. If not, let him practise such mechanical exercises as the reduction of a map to half scale by squares. This will show him how contours normally run and will impress on him that, for example, the contours in a valley run nearly parallel with the river for some distance before crossing the bed and returning nearly parallel on the other side. They do not, as in beginners' exercises, approach the river at right angles, execute a short V-shaped hop over the river and retire round the side of a conical hill.

'Prose' and 'Translation'

As in the learning of languages 'prose' is much more difficult and much more instructive than 'translation'. Fifteen minutes used in drawing a contour map of a particular relief form (and correcting it from an actual map) is worth more than hours spent in 'describing the landforms shown on the sheet provided'.

Ex. The first exercise will therefore be to construct a contour map to specification, as follows:

Map size 6 in. × 6 in.
Scale 1 in. = 1 mile.
Vertical interval 100 ft.
Structure—uniform.
Erosional process—normal.
Stage—early maturity.
Drainage pattern—dendritic.
Amplitude of relief: c. 400 ft.
Main river flows to SE., enters map at 320 ft., falls 10 ft./mile; Valley sides, constant slope about 1 in 50. Main tributary, N–S, falls 40 ft. per mile; Slope of valley sides, constant, about 1 in 20.

Procedure:

1. Draw square outline.
2. Put in the main river (looking like a river, i.e. sinuous lines) and mark the crossing point of the 300-ft. contour 2 in. from entry. The crossing of the 200-ft. contour will be $\dfrac{100}{10} = 10$ in. downstream (off the map).
3. Put in the tributary and mark the approximate height of the main river at the point of confluence (here 4 miles below the 300-ft. contour, i.e 300 ft. − 40 ft. = 260 ft.).
4. Mark the crossing points of each contour on the tributary, these will be $2\frac{1}{2}$ inches apart (40 ft./mile = 100 ft. in $2\frac{1}{2}$ miles).

5. Mark the contour spacing up the main valley sides at the 300-ft. contour crossing. Since the valley-side slope is 1 in 50, the 100-ft. contours will be 5,000 ft., i.e. nearly an inch, apart.

6. Repeat for the tributary valley at the 300-ft. and 200-ft. contour crossings. These will be ⅓ in. apart (1 in 20 = 100 ft. in

$$2,000 \text{ ft.} = \frac{2000}{5840} = c. \text{ 3 per mile}).$$

7. Draw the contours (looking like contours, i.e. flowing lines) through these fixed points.

It will not be necessary to go through all this rigmarole every time one draws a contour map; one soon gets familiar with a contour spacing that (on the scale in use) represents a slope of 1 in 10 or 1 in 20 and with river gradients of 5 ft. per mile or 20 ft. per mile, but until this stage of proficiency is reached it is advisable to construct the guide lines and to mark, at least approximately, the critical points through which the contours are to pass on valley sides and valley bottoms. These simple rules are the 'grammar' of contours, and sound grammar is necessary for the construction of good 'prose'.

More often one will be applying this principle in reverse and estimating gradients from an actual map, with a view to analysing the relief. Such exercises constitute 'translation' from the concise and accurate 'prose' of the map into the looser form of words. The geomorphological evidence, however, does not always stand out obviously on the face of the map. Careful examination, with measurement of distance or slope, is often necessary and the evidence revealed by the measurement can be expressed in figures or in carefully drawn sections.

Section I. The Analysis of Slope

Measurement of Slope

There is much loose talk about 'steep slopes' and 'gentle slopes' without any clear definition of what they mean quantitatively or any precise measurement of the angle of slope. 'Slope' may be expressed in degrees, but more usually as the cotangent of the angle of slope as '1 in 5' (gradient), meaning one unit up for every five units horizontally. This is better than using the cosecant of the angle of slope, i.e. one unit up for every so many units along the ground, because on the map only the horizontal component can be measured, as the map is considered to be viewed vertically.

Ex. To appreciate relative slopes it is helpful to construct slopes of 45°, 30°, 20°, 10°, 5°, &c., and to measure the base of each triangle 1 in. high to find its equivalent gradient. The gradient of some scarps or valley sides should then be measured on the map to see what the appropriate contour spacing looks like. On the 1 in. to 1 mile map the number of contours (inclusive) per inch is as follows:

TABLE 1: *Slope and contour spacing*

Slope	Gradient	Rate of climb, ft./mile	Contours per inch (inclusive)	
			at 100-ft. interval	at 50-ft. interval
11° 19'	1 in 5	1060	10·6 + 1 = 11·6	21 + 1 = 22
6° 45'	10	528	5·28 + 1 = 6·3	11 + 1 = 12
3° 47'	15	352	3·52 + 1 = 4·5	7 + 1 = 8
2° 52'	20	264	2·64 + 1 = 3·6	5 + 1 = 6
2° 18'	25	210	2·1 + 1 = 3·1	4 + 1 = 5
1° 54'	30	176	1·76 + 1 = 2·8	3·5 + 1 = 4·5
1° 26'	40	132	1·32 + 1 = 2·3	2·5 + 1 = 3·5
1° 9'	50	106	1·06 + 1 = 2·1	2·1 + 1 = 3·1
0° 34'	100	53	·53 + 1 = 1·5	1·5 + 1 = 2·5

Ex. A standard scale of such contour spacings can be made on a strip of graph paper, setting off in each 1-in. space the appropriate number of contours by the usual method for the proportional division of a line (Fig. 20). This scale can then be placed on a map and matched up with the contours of any part, whose gradient can then be read off.

Average Slope [1]

Many ill-defined geographical terms such as 'plain' and 'plateau'

[1] See Chester K. Wentworth, 'A Simplified Method of Determining the Average Slope of Land Surfaces', *Amer. Journ. of Sci.*, 1930, p. 184.

46

imply gentle slopes, though the permissible limits of degree of slope are not defined. Others such as 'dissected plateau' imply steep slopes penetrating an area of generally gentle slopes. Others such as 'hilly' imply fairly steep slopes in several directions. What is the general slope of the Central Plateau of France, the Snowdonian mountains or Salis-

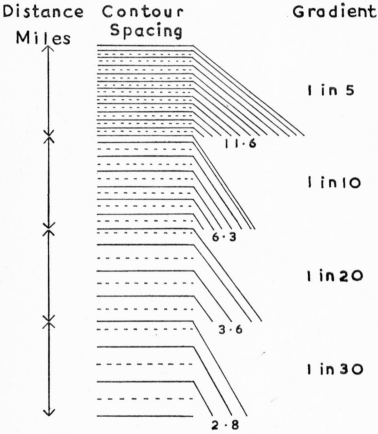

FIG. 20.—Template of standard contour spacings

bury plain? It is clear that the steeper the slope the more contours there will be on the map and a measurement of the number of contours, per unit distance will give a measure of the general slope. Several methods exist for measuring this; the best runs as follows (see Fig. 21):

Ex. 1. Grid the area with parallel straight lines in two directions at right angles.

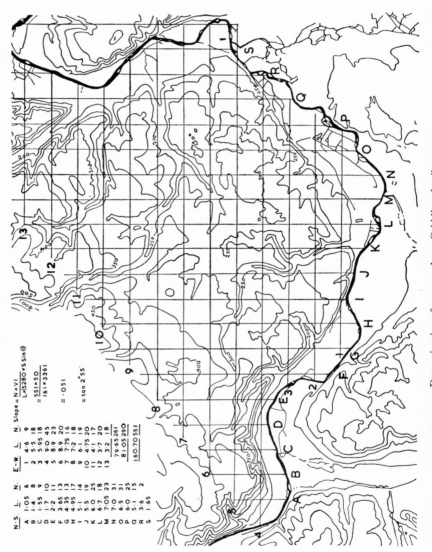

N.-S.	L.	N.		E.-W.	L.	N.	Slope = N × VI
A	1·05	6		1	4·6	9	$L = (5280 × S \sin \theta)$
B	1·4	8		2	5·5	18	
C	1·55	9		3	5·95	18	$= 551 × 50$
D	1·7	10		4	9·0	45	$= 161 × 336 l$
E	2·2	11		5	8·9	23	
F	3·65	13		6	8·9	20	$= \cdot 051$
G	4·35	13		7	7·75	16	
H	4·95	17		8	7·2	18	
J	5·1	14		9	6·1	19	$= \tan 2° 55$
K	5·5	19		10	4·75	20	
L	6·0	25		11	4·1	17	
M	6·7	18		12	3·7	20	
N	7·05	23		13	3·2	18	
O	7·0	31			79·65	261	
P	6·5	31			81·05	290	
Q	6·0	25			160·70	551	
R	5·1	15					
S	1·65	2					

FIG. 21.—Determination of average slope. Grid lines ½ mile apart

2. Proceed along each grid line counting the number of times it crosses a contour. Set down the total for each line and add them together.
3. Measure the total length of the grid lines and determine the number of crossings per mile of grid line.
4. Multiply the crossings per mile by the contour interval.
5. Divide this product by 3,361. This constant, 3,361, is 5,280 (feet in a mile) × 0·6366 (mean of all possible values of sin θ, where θ is the horizontal angle between the contour and the grid line).

The result is the tangent of the angle of general slope which can, if desired, be converted to degrees from a table of tangents. Suitable maps for repeating this exercise can be found in almost any slightly dissected plateau area, e.g. Cotswold 'dip slope', sub-Eocene surface on the Chilterns, Northern Pennines, Longmynd. The example given above is from the partially gravel-covered chalk slope north of Reading.

Valley Forms

It has been said, with some truth, that the valley is the cause of all topographic forms under 'normal' erosion. The processes of weathering are numerous and varied, mechanical, chemical, and biological, but their effect on relief is small compared with the power of stream erosion. Obviously stream erosion is most powerful and its effects are most pronounced in the neighbourhood of rivers and large streams which exert an effective base-level control: within this zone the dictum quoted above is true, but away from stream influence it begins to lose its validity. In the evolution of relief in the normal erosional cycle we recognize a stage, known as 'maturity', at which the headward and sideways erosion of streams has extended its influence so far that adjacent valley systems meet at the divide and begin to destroy it.

Prior to maturity, however, the interfluve retains its previous form, altered only by weathering, and the relief of such interfluves may be regarded as a survival, slightly modified perhaps, from the previous cycle. In the present chapter we are concerned with the forms of the land within the zone of influence of the river or stream; later we shall consider the region of the divide.

The significance of valley shape in transverse and longitudinal profile will be considered below. In any careful analysis of relief these objective, mechanical exercises for the analysis of form should be undertaken as a first step.

Profile and Section Drawing

In the construction of geological sections, described on p. 28, the whole depth of the face exposed by cutting the section is laid bare and its structure is shown. The outline of such a section, i.e. the intersection of the section with the land surface, is its 'profile'. In the investigation of surface morphology, so long as its relationship to structure is not under consideration, we are concerned only with the profile, which is a line and not a surface. The purpose of a profile is to show, with precision, the form of the land, which could be envisaged, in general terms, from the contours. The object is twofold, first to discover significant facts for oneself and second to demonstrate them and to prove their reality to the reader, for no physiographic assertion is axiomatic. What an observer sees in a landscape, or thinks he sees, is not evidence; each statement should be supported by the fullest possible proof. Since not all forms are significant the choice of the line of section is of vital importance, and here the personal element is apt to enter. It is sometimes possible to select an unrepresentative section to provide 'proof' of a particular hypothesis which other sections would disprove. This is a practice against which one should set one's face; one must satisfy oneself honestly that the whole picture of the relief is consistent with the explanation put forward. Some general principles to guide one in the selection of section lines will be given, as they arise, in each physiographic type. One line of section whose usefulness is beyond doubt, whose objectivity is above reproach and whose selection is inevitable is the longitudinal profile (thalweg) of a river valley.

Stream Profiles or Thalwegs

Ex. The thalweg (= valley way) of a river is the curve of the river course from source to mouth; it is a profile along the winding line of the valley floor. For practice in constructing thalwegs short rivers with marked breaks of slope are best, e.g. the Lake District; the Upper Towy drainage, Dartmoor; Bowland Forest; the Forest of Dean. The procedure is described below.

Since the graph-paper edge cannot be placed along a winding river, the usual method of section drawing is here inapplicable, and the proper procedure is to measure the distance between points of known altitude in the valley floor and to plot the distances so obtained against altitude. Unfortunately the number of points of fixed altitude is limited, in general, to the crossing places of the contours, while the slope between these fixed points is unknown. A little additional information can sometimes be obtained from spot heights on the flood plain or bench-marks on bridges. But such information must be used with caution and allowance must be made for the height of bridges above the flood plain, which may be considerable. Caution should also be exercised in the use of the 50-ft. interpolated contours of the 4th and later editions of the Ordnance Survey Maps. It is better to use the valley floor and flood plain (if any) rather than the water surface or stream bed, because the information on the map relates to the land;

if this practice is followed consistently errors will be avoided and the result satisfactory within the limitations of the map. Field work can, of course, be made to amplify the information on the map and the profile can be measured by clinometer, level or aneroid, but such is beyond our present scope. Distances may be measured with a measuring wheel or with a piece of cotton which must be bent to follow the course of the river. Neither method is quite accurate and each inter-contour distance should be measured at least twice or until a consistent measurement is obtained.

The inter-contour distances thus obtained are now plotted on squared paper with convenient horizontal and vertical scales, which must, of course, be shown. It is advisable to exaggerate the vertical scale considerably to bring out differences of gradient. If this is not done fictitious irregularities, or regularities, may be produced by failure to draw the line through the centre of the dot.

The finished section will show at a glance the form of the curve of the river which may be—

1. The concave graded curve of maturity. In this case the steepness of the curve, taken in conjunction with the volume, may betray early or late maturity.

2. Convexities, or breaks of slope, which may be due to—

(a) arrested grading by resistant rocks, which may be verified by reference to the geological map and to other relief features produced by the outcrop in question.

(b) Differences in rate of valley lowering due to change of rock type, e.g. limestone. This differs in degree only from (a).

(c) Glaciation; the convexities in this case will probably be associated with flattened reaches and even reversed slopes above the break of slope.

(d) Rejuvenation; in this case the curves above and below the 'knick point' will probably be graded.

3. (Rarely) Prematurely flat reaches (cf. 2(c)) or sudden changes from steep to flat slopes downstream. This may be due to the upstream encroachment of alluviation and can be verified by the cross section of the valley floor which will be flat (alluvial) below and steep-sided and narrower above the break.

The attainment of maturity is reached earlier in large valleys than in small and in main streams than in tributaries. On the other hand very small streams and headwater streams, never having reached a condition of grade, usually contain irregularities of little significance. Consequently this method usually yields best results in streams of intermediate size and in the tributaries of larger rivers. Fig. 22 shows the profiles of the tributaries of the lower course of the River Wye where it flows through the Forest of Dean. There is a strong agreement in form, each consisting of three reaches, the lowest graded to the present

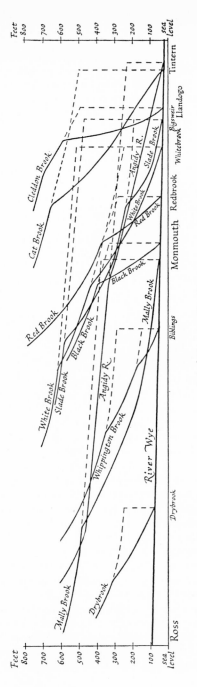

FIG. 22.—Thalweg profiles of the River Wye and tributaries

Scale of Miles along River Wye
1 0 2 4 6 8 10

Scale along tributaries exaggerated 5 times

River Wye, the next graded to about *250* ft. higher and the next to about *500* ft. higher; i.e. two rejuvenation stages are suggested.

The tabulated inter-contour distances reveal knick points more clearly than the drawn section. The 'normal' form of a river profile is a curve concave upwards, i.e. the inter-contour spacings decrease in length upstream. If at any point they increase in length a break of slope (knick point) is revealed.

TABLE 2: *River Tavy* (*Devonshire*)

Feet	Yards		Feet	Yards	
Source–1800	450	450	850–800	400	1000
1800–1750	480		800–750	840	
1750–1700	850	1330	750–700	690	1530
1700–1650	350		700–650	1250	
1650–1600	400	750	650–600	570	1820
1600–1550	250		600–550	1000	
1550–1500	800	1050			
1500–1450	280		550–500	450	1450
1450–1400	1000	1280	500–450	480	
1400–1350	660		450–400	1100	1580
1350–1300	470	1130	400–350	950	
1300–1250	950		350–300	2400	3350
1250–1200	250	1200	300–250	1660	
1200–1150	380		250–200	2260	3920
1150–1100	300	680	200–150	2620	
1100–1050	390		150–100	2520	5140
1050–1000	500	890	100– 50	2480	
1000– 950	660		50– Sea Level . >	6650	9130
950– 900	230	890		28320	
900– 850	600				
	10250		TOTAL	38,570 yards	

From the 50-ft. inter-contour distances listed in Table 2 the profile of the River Tavy seems to show several well-defined breaks of slope, especially at 1,700, 1,400, 1,250, 950, 550, 400, 300, and 150 ft. Are these real? or are they produced by the map maker? Suspicion is aroused by the alternation of large with small intercepts, e.g. between 1,800 and 1,400 ft., between 1,000 and 550 ft., and between 450 and 250 ft., and the suspicion grows as we recollect that the 50-ft. contours are interpolated. So let us fall back on the 100-ft. surveyed contours, shown in the second column. The genuineness of the breaks at 1,700, 1,400, 1,200, and 600 ft. receives support, the others remain gravely suspect. We shall have cause again later to be on our guard against reliance on the interpolated contour (p. 70).

It should not be necessary to emphasize that map studies of this type are only preliminary steps in morphological analysis and that the reality of knick points must be checked in the field by careful survey before they are accepted and before they are called in evidence for any interpretation of geomorphological history.

Valley Cross Profiles

The transverse section of a valley is very revealing and would seem to be an obvious direction to select for profile drawing. Unfortunately the attempt to draw accurate profiles on the 1-in. scale meets with serious practical difficulties, especially if the valley is steep-sided. In a glaciated trough-valley, for example, the contours may be almost touching each other and the displacement of a contour by a fiftieth of an inch in the process of transference to the squared paper may materially distort the form of the valley. Sections of gorge-like valleys on the 1-in. scale are therefore not reliable and may be definitely misleading; they are fit only for the demonstration of general principles. On the 6-in. scale, however, this limitation is much less serious and, whenever feasible, this scale should be used for the study of steep-sided valleys. But even if we adopt the 6-in. scale we do not avoid all the difficulties; for the contour interval of 100 ft. (except in a few fortunate areas, e.g. E. Yorks, where a 25-ft. contour interval was adopted in the original survey), provides fixed altitudes at too widely spaced intervals, and the joining up of these fixed points provides abundant opportunities for doubt and error. A few scattered spot heights give additional precise information between contours and the section can often be selected to pass through one or more of these. If and when the 25-ft. contours on the new 1/25,000 map are surveyed (at present they are interpolated) the value of this excellent map will be greatly enhanced.

Despite these limitations the valley cross-profile may display valuable evidence of origin. It may be

(1) The wide, open ⌣⌣⌣⌣ of post maturity.

(2) The narrow V of youth.

(3) The asymetrical form of, e.g. subsequent valleys at the foot of escarpments.

(4) The flat floored form of aggraded valleys ⌣___⌿ with wide flood plain.

(5) The steep-sided ∪ of glaciation.

(6) The ⊔ of gorge valleys in thick beds of pure limestone.

(7) The narrow ⊔ of canyons; some glacial overflows approximate to this shape.

(8) Breaks of slope or 'Valley-in-valley' form. ⌐V This may be due to:

(a) Incomplete grading of slopes in regions of beds of differing degrees of resistance.

(b) Rejuvenation, i.e. presence of two or more erosional cycles.

(c) Complex forms, e.g. glacial trough in the floor of an old water-cut valley.
(d) Two or more stages of glaciation.
(e) Terrace formation, though this will seldom be recognizable unless the contour interval is small.

Reconstructed Thalwegs

Any of the characteristics listed above will persist over considerable distances along the river course; profiles should therefore be drawn at

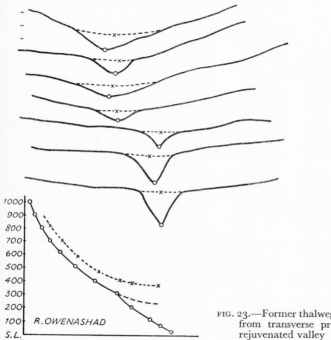

FIG. 23.—Former thalweg reconstructed from transverse profiles across a rejuvenated valley

intervals to ascertain how far any characteristic form extends up or down the stream. Fig. 23 shows a number of profiles drawn in this way across the valley of the Owenashad, a tributary of the Blackwater in Co. Cork. The valley-in-valley form, here due to rejuvenation, persists over a distance of about 3 miles. The surviving floor and sides of the old valley are used as a basis for the reconstruction of the old valley cross-profile by means of which the altitude of the pre-rejuvenation valley floor may be approximately deduced. These heights may then be inserted on the thalweg section already drawn and are found to lie on or near a graded curve, but at some height above the present valley floor in the rejuvenated reach. This graded curve may be found to be

5

continuous with the upper reaches of the thalweg (cf. p. 52) above the knick point (rejuvenation head) as in Fig. 24, which illustrates the principle in diagrammatic form.

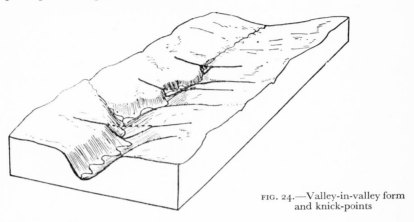

FIG. 24.—Valley-in-valley form and knick-points

Crest-line Profiles

In some relief forms a special significance attaches to the form of the divides. These are the places furthest removed from valley excavation, either by river or glacier, and are therefore the most likely refuges of vanishing relief; as an instance we may quote the survival of the Schooley peneplain on the ridge crests of the Northern Appalachians.[1] In the unfolding of the geographical cycle the stage known as 'maturity' is said to be reached when the recession of valley-side slopes in adjacent valleys has caused them to meet and so to begin the demolition of the divide. Up to this point, therefore, but not after it, the interfluve crest has a special significance and a section along or across it may be expected to demonstrate a feature of interpretative value. To give the best possible picture the section line should be chosen to run along the crest, which will not be a straight but a winding line.

Ex. The construction of a profile along a crooked, winding line by the simple standard method of placing the edge of the paper along the line of section involves continual moving and twisting of the paper. In the process it is likely that the paper will slip and errors will be introduced. The difficulty is the same as that experienced in drawing the longitudinal profile of a river and, if desired, the same technique can be employed. The crest line is pencilled in on the map and the inter-contour distances measured. This is not really necessary as the errors introduced by slipping of the paper will be errors of distance, which seldom matters, and not of height which does. Such sections can reveal

[1] Douglas Johnson, *Stream Sculpture on the Atlantic Slope*, 1931.

the existence and the form of wind-gaps and other down-sags and may bring to light evidence relating to an earlier erosion cycle, e.g. the crest-line of the South Downs (Brighton and Worthing sheet).

Projected Profiles

Ex. Since distance does not often matter it is legitimate to fore-shorten the crest-line profile by projecting it on to a straight line running parallel to the main direction of the divide, as shown in Fig. 25. The most accurate method of constructing such profiles is to pin the map on a drawing board in such a way that the line of section is parallel to one edge. Then pin the section paper parallel with this edge and a convenient distance above the line of section. A T-square can then be set against this or the opposite edge and slid along until its ruling edge is tangent to the closed end of the contour. This is the point at which the crest-line climbs above this contour and can be transferred to the section paper. The effect is to reproduce a view of the crest-line such as a photograph might show, but with this advantage that the lens of the imaginary camera is always at the same level as the crest and is always opposite the point projected. The projection, in fact, is by parallel lines (orthographic) and not, as in a photograph, by convergent lines (stereographic); heights are therefore actual, not apparent, heights. This is known as a projected profile.

Multiple Projected Profiles

The term projected profile is usually applied to a multiple application of the above principle. A strip of country is selected for the experiment and each crest-line is projected in turn from the foreground

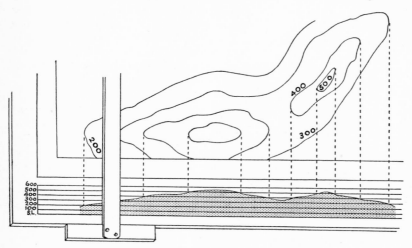

FIG. 25.—Construction of projected profile

towards the background, thus reproducing a panorama of crests such as would be seen by the eye or a camera, but at its true, not its apparent, height (Fig. 26). The usual practice is to omit all background features that are obscured by foreground features of greater height, as they would actually be in a view, but this seems an unnecessary and unwise waste of the advantages conferred by the method. There may be ridges of significant altitude and form obscured by foreground features. To omit these would be to throw away valuable evidence. They may well be inserted, even if dotted to show that they are not 'visible'.

The chief use of the method is in detecting and demonstrating dissected peneplains; examples may be seen in

Barrell, J., *Amer. Journ. of Sci.*, 1920;
Hollingworth, S. E., *Proc. Yorks. Geol. Soc.*, 1936;
Miller, A. A., *Geogr. Journ*, 1937.

Super(im)posed Profiles

It sometimes happens that a projected profile fails to meet the case; the belt of country to be analysed may, for instance, not be a rectangular strip but a crescent or some irregular shape. The choice of a suitable single direction of projection then becomes impossible. In the case of a semicircular belt of coastal plateau peripheral to a circular highland mass, e.g. the Lake District, it is clear that such terrain can be dealt with by projected profiles only in bits.[1] If it were dealt with in one, quite apart from the fact that its width is too great, the highland at the centre would obscure the effect of the proximal and distal horns of the crescent. In such cases as this we can make use of an alternative construction, drawing each profile independently and then tracing them off, one by one on to a single sheet of tracing paper, taking care, of course, to keep the vertical scale and the base line (sea level) the same in every case. This method has an advantage over the projected profile that the section can be displaced laterally so as to arrange the coincidence of one significant feature. Let us suppose, for instance, that we are dealing with a series of raised beaches and that many of the individual sections display an old cliff-line at the back of the beach at a constant level of 100 ft. We can now arrange our sections so that the *position* of the cliff-foot coincides on all sections on which the feature appears (cf. device on p. 61). We must not, of course, displace the sections *vertically* to arrange coincidence of *altitude* of the cliff-foot, though even this might be legitimate if we were concerned with the *form* and not the altitude of raised beaches and their back-slopes.

So far we have considered the superposition of ridge and spur profiles, but simple sections along any number of parallel straight lines may be superposed. Such sections, in that their position is quite

[1] See Hollingworth, above.

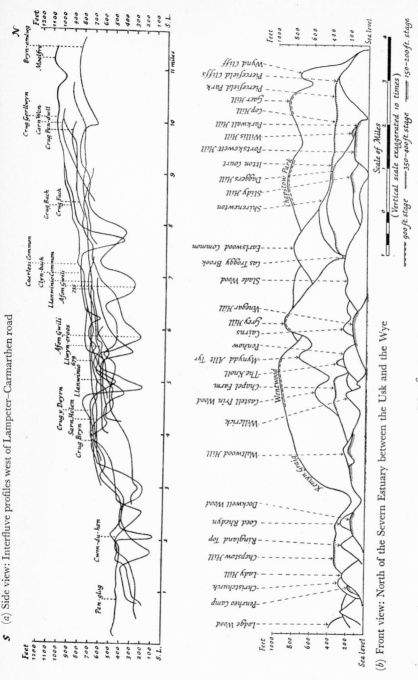

(a) Side view: Interfluve profiles west of Lampeter–Carmarthen road

(b) Front view: North of the Severn Estuary between the Usk and the Wye

FIG. 26.—PROJECTED PROFILES

independent of personal selection or bias, may be said to present an entirely objective picture of the relief, but they inevitably contain much irrelevant stuff that obscures the clarity of, for example, a dissected plateau. For the line of section will not often pass through the summit of a hill, whose altitude would be significant; it is likely to cut at random across spurs, producing on the section the illusion of summits that are entirely fictitious, or to run along a hillside producing an equally false impression of a plateau. Only when considerable areas of plateau survive, so extensive and dominating of the relief that they can hardly be missed by randomly directed sections, is this method anything less than misleading in the detection of erosion surfaces and summit planes. It may be laid down as a general principle that in any profile or set of profiles in which the summits are going to be interpreted as significant, the profiles, should pass along *all* summits and *only* along summits. But these random sections do show, what the strict ridge profile cannot, the depth of the valleys and the amplitude of relief, i.e. the difference in altitude between valley bottoms and ridge tops (see below).

Spur Profiles

A dilemma that presents itself at an early stage in the construction of ridge profiles is this; what are we to do when the ridge comes to an end at a gap? The crest of the South Downs may be considered as an example. It is breached by the water-gaps of the Ouse, Adur, and Arun, and it sags to numerous wind-gaps between. The answer is that the section should be taken down the crest of the spur and up the other side on to the continuation of the ridge. As has been pointed out above, the depth of both wind-gaps and water-gaps are of great significance in the analysis of relief. The wind-gaps reveal the level of the river before capture, the depth of the water-gaps displays the amplitude of relief. Furthermore, if the water-gap has been cut in two stages (i.e. two cycles of erosion) the evidence of the earlier cycle is most likely to be preserved on the spurs leading down to the river, for these, being divides, are exempt from erosion, though vulnerable to weathering.

Profiles down the crests of spurs are thus well worth drawing, though the facets preserved on them are often too small to be detectable on the 1-in. map, and often demand supplementary information by levelling in the field. A word of warning is also needed against the danger of accepting evidence from a single spur, on which a facet may occur for some purely fortuitous reason.

Staggered Spur Profiles

Spur sections, like crest-line sections, may be rearranged for greater clarity. Those in Fig. 27 have been pushed sideways, like the wings of stage scenery, to give a clear view up the rather winding Mawddach estuary from Barmouth to Dolgelley. Nearly all show 'steps' at about

200 ft., 500 ft., and 1,000 ft. An imaginary shelf (unshaded) has been laid on each of these in the diagram, and the original form of the 'risers' has been reconstructed by shading.

FIG. 27.—Staggered spur profiles. Mawddach Estuary

The Amplitude of Relief

By this is meant the vertical distance between valley bottom and hill crests. It can therefore be demonstrated visually by combining thalweg profiles and ridge profiles (Fig. 28). But care must be taken to keep the two 'in step', for their lengths in miles will not be the same, since the divides are generally straighter and shorter than the winding course of the river. It is better, therefore, to check them from a number of cross-sections at intervals down the valley. Where tributaries enter, the divide really passes round the head of the tributary, but it will normally be sufficient to interrupt the crest-line profiles at such points.

On the theory of the erosion cycle the amplitude of relief increases from the source region, where it may be nil, to a maximum in the region of maturity, thereafter declining to the mouth, where it again becomes nil. This, of course, would only be true in a drainage of uniform texture of rock, for differential rates of wastage of divides cause greater amplitude in regions of resistant rock, as can be seen from the course of the Rhymney across the varied rocks of the coalfield and the coastal plateau of South Wales shown above, or from the River Thames above and in the Goring Gap.

Quite obviously, however, there is another factor to be considered, namely the available amplitude, i.e. the elevation of the initial surface above the base level. It is clear that a river flowing from a high 'old land' across an emerged sea floor of low altitude can have only a small amplitude of relief in its lower reaches, even when it has reached maturity, contrasted markedly with a high amplitude that is possible within the 'old land'. It is worth noting that the divides, in such cases, will preserve their flat form for a very long while, since divide wastage depends on the recession of valley-side slopes which is very slow where gradients are small, i.e. where there is only a small available fall over

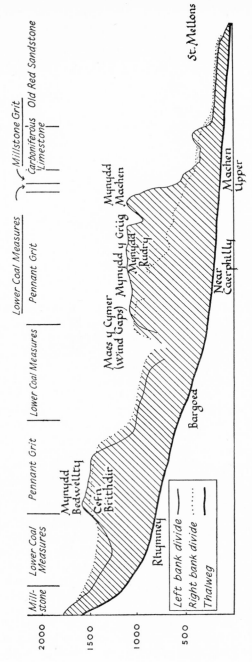

FIG. 28.—Amplitude of relief: River Rhymney

a fairly long distance. Many low terraces and coastal plateaux owe their good state of preservation to this arrangement. This can be seen in the last 4 miles of the Rhymney valley, and is shown diagrammatically in Fig. 29, in which the spacing of streams (texture of dissection) is the same in both cases.

Ex. Methods have been suggested [1] for preparing a map of available relief by dividing the map into squares and inserting in each square the difference in altitude between the highest and lowest points present. This will only present a true picture if the squares are large enough for each to contain a summit and a valley floor, ensuring that the maximum amplitude is represented. It could be tried for a whole country using, say, five-mile squares, but is of little value for the detection and distinction of minor physiographic regions. Certain resemblances will

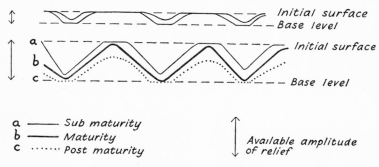

FIG. 29.—Available amplitude of relief

readily be detected to the method used for constructing relative slope maps on p. 48.

Generalized Contours

It has been stated above that facets representing ancient surfaces, structural or erosional in origin, are best preserved on ridge crests. Often the development of streams on such a surface, perhaps consequent on its initial slope, has dissected it deeply. In such cases the initial form of the plateau can often be reconstructed by drawing generalized contours tangent to the existing contours on the interfluves.

Ex. The example shown here (Fig. 30) is based on the dip slope of the Chiltern Hills between Nettlebed and Chesham but the actual contours have been very much straightened and simplified to clarify the mode of construction. Remembering that the only significant

[1] Guy-Harold Smith, 'The Relative Relief of Ohio', *Geog. Rev.*, 1935, p. 272; and G. H. Dury, 'Quantitative Measurement of Available Relief and Texture of Dissection', *Geol. Mag.*, 1951, p. 339; and W. S. Glock, 'Available Relief as a Factor of Control in the Profile of Land Form', *Journ. of Geology*, 1932, p. 74.

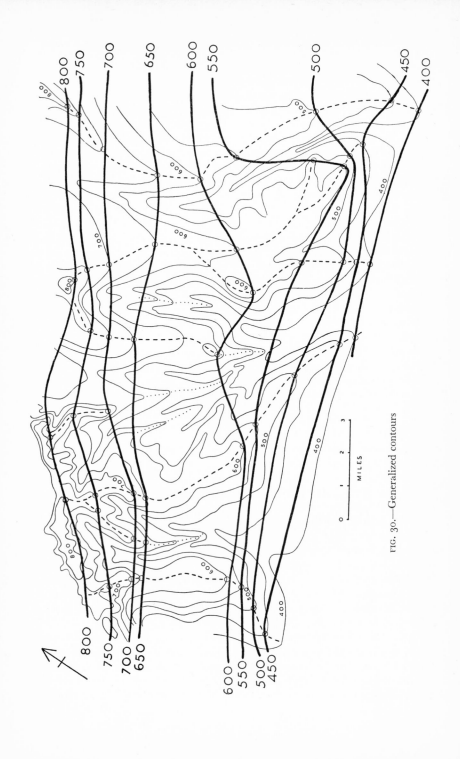

FIG. 30.—Generalized contours

interfluves are those which have not yet passed maturity, a line (heavy broken line in the figure) is drawn down the backbone of each significant spur, and at the point furthest downhill at which it crosses each contour a circle is placed. The generalized contours at each contour interval are then drawn across the dissecting valleys, joining these circles. Spurs which have passed maturity in the erosional cycle, and thus have become sharp and narrow, have no significance and must be ignored in the reconstruction. The crest-lines of such spurs are marked with lines of dots on Fig. 30. Erosion has reduced them below the general level of the initial surface.

Hill-top Envelope Maps

If dissection has proceeded to such a stage that the interfluves have been partially destroyed and lost their continuity of slope, the initial surface may still be reconstructed, though with less certainty, as follows.

Ex. A piece of tracing paper is placed over the map and every closed hill-top contour is traced off and its altitude recorded in the space enclosed. Generalized contours are then drawn in on the assumption that these hills reached to the initial surface (Fig. 31). In practice several hills will fail to fall into the pattern because they have been reduced below the initial surface, and this is most likely with hills close to streams whose sideways encroachment has attacked them early and powerfully. The coastal pleateaux of South Wales (Pontypridd and Barry sheet) provide excellent material for this exercise, so do those of South Devon (Plymouth and Torquay sheets).

Area-Height Curves

This curve shows the proportion of land in a given area at each altitude, or, in practice, between each pair of adjacent contours; it thus shows the relative amounts of highland, lowland, or land at any stated intermediate altitude. According to the principles underlying the concept of the geographical cycle, slopes recede progressively headwards from base level towards summits and divides. The average form of the surface at and after maturity, should therefore be a curve of steadily decreasing slope from the summit of divides to the base level. Any departure from this form requires an explanation which may be found in unattained maturity or arrested attainment of maturity, for either of which one or more of many explanations may be offered. The area-height curve is thus usually worth drawing and will often provide the evidence for important conclusions on physiographic history.

Ex. The curve is obtained by plotting area against altitude, and the chief difficulties that arise in construction are those of estimating the area at each altitude. The obvious method is by means of the planimeter, but in practice this is too laborious, for it involves the measurement of the area above every contour in turn on every hill and ridge.

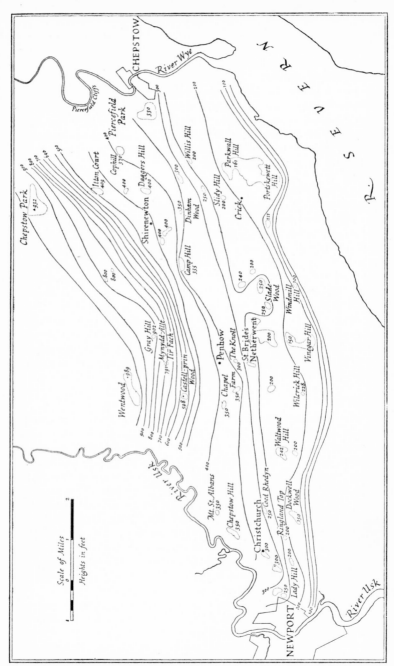

FIG. 31.—Reconstructed extent of marine platforms

In practice the method of 'sampling' is used, the samples being taken along evenly spaced parallel lines drawn across the area to be examined, and, though the method is not exact, the error is small if a sufficient number of samples is taken. In Fig. 32 the total length of all the *a*'s is regarded as expressing the area above 700 ft., the total length of the *b*'s as expressing the area between 600 ft. and 700 ft., and the total length of *c*'s as expressing the area between 500 ft. and 600 ft., &c.

We begin by drawing a number, at least 12, of equally spaced parallel lines across the area to be studied and, dealing with each line

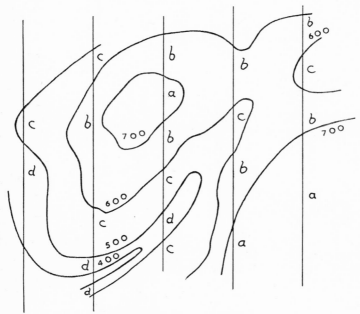

FIG. 32.—Estimating area by sampling along parallel lines

in turn, we measure the length of the intercept between each pair of adjacent contours. The unit used does not matter, but it should be small enough not to require subdivision, a tenth of an inch is a suitable unit available on a ruler, but for closely spaced contours a millimetre may be necessary. The measured lengths are set down in column form and the total intercepts between each pair of contours is added up; this figure is proportional to the area between those contours.

This exercise takes up a great deal of time. If worked in class the hard labour can be divided up, each line being allocated to a pair of students, one to measure the lengths and to dictate to the other who writes them down. Table 3, which shows the method of booking, was

TABLE 3: *Length (in mm.) of intercepts between contours (50-ft. interval) on parallel North–South lines at 1-in. interval.*

Torquay Sheet. 5th (Relief) Edition

Height in feet	A	B	C	D	E	F	G	H	I	J	K	L	M	N	O	P	Q	R	S	Total intercepts	Summed total intercepts
1600–1650		5	9																	14	14
1550–1600		18	14																	32	46
1500–1550	12	14	8																	34	80
1450–1500	13	20	31	5																69	149
1400–1450	27	37	11	4																79	228
1350–1400	16	16	20	14																66	294
1300–1350	24	19	15	19																77	371
1250–1300	20	17	29	21																87	458
1200–1250	22	5	20	15	5															67	525
1150–1200	14	4	21	21	9															69	594
1100–1150	8	3	11	27	16			4												69	663
1050–1100	11	14	16	12	11			10												74	737
1000–1050	1	6	6	20	9			1												43	780
950–1000	1	12	10	9	31		2	2												67	847
900– 950	5	27	12	9	38		2	3												96	943
850– 900	3	26	4	19	15	8	1	2												78	1021
800– 850	4	5	4	13	8	8	1	9	5											57	1078

750– 800	3	4	3	10	6	8	5	5	5	2										51	1129
700– 750	12	7	2	19	7	26	2	2	7	4										88	1217
650– 700	24	12	3	12	9	20	3	2	5	16										106	1323
600– 650	21	1	2	4	13	30	6	2	7	8	6	16	4	2						122	1445
550– 600	2	1	1	8	27	35	14	9	10	5	14	13	5	4		1		4	1	154	1599
500– 550	7	3	1	15	27	22	37	37	29	36	33	12	21	8	5	11	5	11	5	325	1924
450– 500	8	17	1	13	57	24	39	46	61	32	39	25	42	19	32	15	3	15	8	496	2420
400– 450	15	14	18	12	35	69	54	57	83	73	67	26	32	28	28	29	12	26	8	686	3106
350– 400	24	18	26	11	44	64	66	80	37	62	104	46	23	41	32	29	21	27	12	767	3873
300– 350	16	41	29	26	40	91	60	81	65	46	63	64	47	58	31	32	45	17	19	871	4744
250– 300	16	17	15	29	35	49	67	44	68	53	60	55	72	56	32	16	25	21	27	757	5501
200– 250	15	19	35	54	33	40	71	29	43	50	53	84	50	61	27	59	53	24	23	823	6324
150– 200	13	16	38	27	22	14	42	25	36	40	48	63	65	43	28	40	64	38	21	683	7007
100– 150	10	37	14	24	19	15	24	39	19	66	70	42	44	13	31	26	23	13	12	541	7548
50– 100	16	10	5	24	23	22	27	15	22	36	22	23	53	29	79	71	31	29	14	551	8099
S.L.– 50	25	7	.	45	28	8	17	6	17	8	5	39	24	1	19	2	17	21	11	300	8399
Sum of intercepts	408	472	434	541	567	553	540	510	519	537	584	508	482	363	354	331	299	245	161	8399	
Measured line of section	446	459	469	553	569	574	598	514	574	630	592	528	452	402	400	373	376	289	250		
Error	−38	+13	−35	−12	−2	−21	−58	−4	−55	−93	−8	−20	+30	−39	−47	−42	−78	−44	−89		
% Error	9	3	8	2	0·3	4	10	0·8	10	15	1	4	7	10	12	11	21	15	31		

prepared in this way, each pair doing two long or three short lines. Afterwards, as a check on the accuracy of the student, it is advisable to add up all the intercepts on each line and to compare them with the total measured length of the line to see if they agree. Such a check on Table 3 shows that the two pairs who were made responsible for the last six lines were thoroughly unreliable, as were the pair who did line J.

An inspection of the final totals will show at a glance at what height the majority of the land lies and this may be presented visually by plotting the totals against altitude (Curve a, Fig. 33). On a graded slope the totals would increase steadily towards sea level and the curve obtained would be a curve of steadily decreasing slope. In Table 3 this is not the case; the greatest area of land in a single 50 ft. band lies between 300 and 350 ft. and the bulk of the land lies between 100 and 500 ft., while the areas both above and below are relatively small, i.e. there is an unduly wide expanse between 100 and 500, which on closer inspection appears to have a double maximum at 200–250 and at 300–350 ft. This may be so, but if the profile of the River Tavy p. 53) is referred to, the tendency for long reaches to alternate with short reaches will be noticed as a feature of peculiarly frequent recurrence; it is as well to accept the positioning of the interpolated 50-ft. contours with reserve.

The Hypsometric Curve

This, however, is not the form in which the relationship is usually presented. Most authors prefer to show the hypsographic or hypsometric curve which expresses the *total* area above each altitude, i.e. the land above 700 ft. includes all land between 700 and 800 + all land between 800 and 900 + all land between 900 and 1,000 and so on to the highest land present on the measured sections. So the intercepts are summed, as in the last column, and these summed intercepts, plotted against altitude, give the hypsometric curve, which reflects the mean slope over the whole area at each height.

It is clear that such a curve can detect flat surfaces only if such features maintain a constant altitude in relation to sea level over the whole of the area sampled. They are therefore useful in detecting and demonstrating raised beaches and erosion surfaces which are unwarped and horizontal. If inclined surfaces are suspected then only a small area at a time should be sampled, an area over which the feature will not have declined significantly in altitude laterally.

The Clinographic Curve

The curve obtained by plotting area against altitude on a slope continuous and constant in one direction (e.g. a writing desk) is a straight line, but the curve of area to height on a right cone with slopes

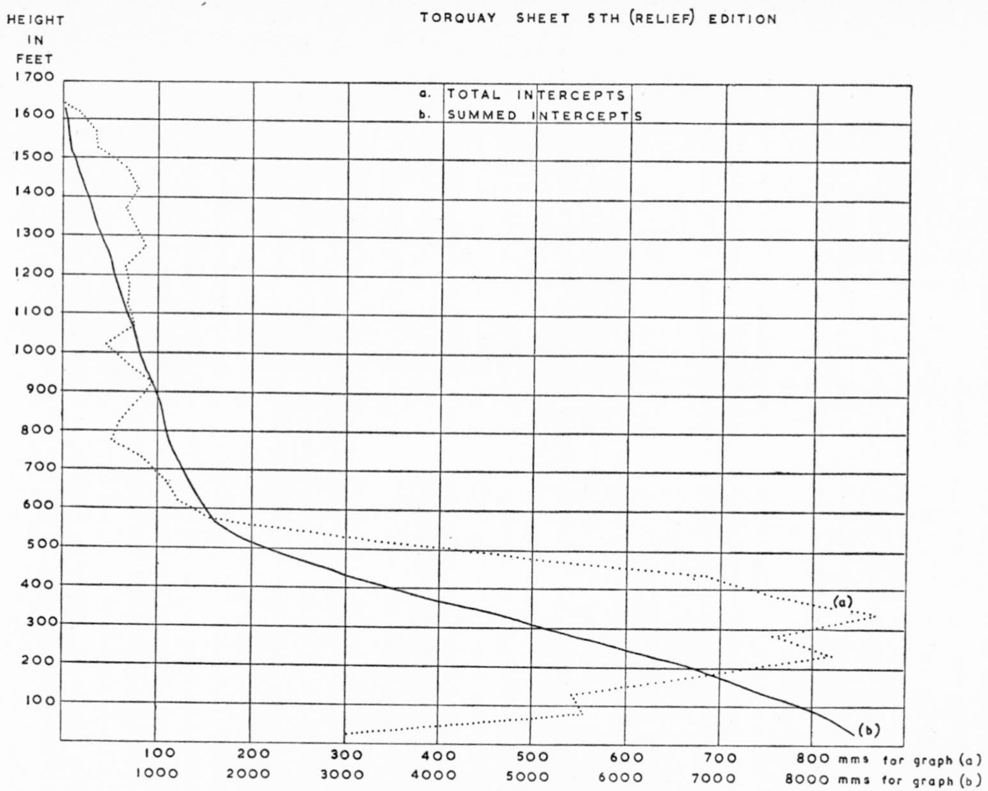

TORQUAY SHEET 5TH (RELIEF) EDITION

HEIGHT
IN
FEET

a. TOTAL INTERCEPTS
b. SUMMED INTERCEPTS

FIG. 33.—Hypsometric curve and area-height curve

6

in all directions radially is not; it will be concave upwards even though the sides of the cone are straight. The land surface being analysed may partake in some degree of either of these forms, but the more it is dissected into hills with slopes in all directions the closer its mean form approximates to the cone. Some concavity of the hypsometric curve must therefore be expected quite apart from any flattening of the land at lower levels. Thus a diminution downhill of the intercept lengths is even more significant than it seemed at first. In essentially conical landscapes, such as a whole island, the clinographic curve [1] is to be preferred, but it would be misleading if applied to, say, the dip slope of the Cotswold Hills.

These methods should be compared with those described on p. 49 for calculating average slope, where a factor is introduced to compensate for the horizontal angle between contour and grid line.

Altitude Frequency Curves

These are constructed on the same geomorphological principle as the last two exercises, namely that hill-tops offer the last refuge for vanishing relief. A statistical count of the number of hill-tops in each altitude range may reveal a preponderant frequency at certain levels. This in turn may give a clue to the presence, in former times, of a preponderance of land area at this level, i.e. flat land, perhaps representing an erosion level, now dissected into hill-tops. Conversely the steeper slopes separating one flat from the next will, on dissection, produce few or no hill-tops, and there will be a frequency minimum at such levels.

If hill-top numbers or spot heights are used, it is a weakness that the method emphasizes number and minimises area. Thus a small shelf carved up into four culminations counts 4, but a large undissected gently sloping plateau counts 0. Dissected regions thus score over undissected. This difficulty can be overcome and perfect objectivity can be retained by the method of random sampling; the area is divided up into equal squares and the highest point in each square is recorded. But the highest point may not be a summit but on a slope, and would thus be without significance on the very principle that underlies the method. The method is extremely laborious, but the results obtained are interesting [2] (see Fig. 34).

Facet Maps

By means of such devices as have been described the existence of certain 'facets' of the landscape may be detected, such as valley-bottom flats, plateau tops, bevelled hill crests, valley-side slopes, sea-cliffs, &c.

---

[1] For method of construction see Hanson Lowe, *Geol. Mag.*, 1935.

[2] See Baulig, 'The Changing Sea Level', *Inst. of Brit. Geog.*, 1935; and Hollingworth, *Quart. Journ. Geol. Soc.*, 1938, p. 55.

In rejuvenated landscapes there may be more than one facet on a valley side and more than one erosion surface separated from the next by a steeper sloping 'facet'. Adjacent facets are separated by a break of slope, a feature which is always geomorphologically significant.

It is rarely possible to delimit such facets with any certainty from

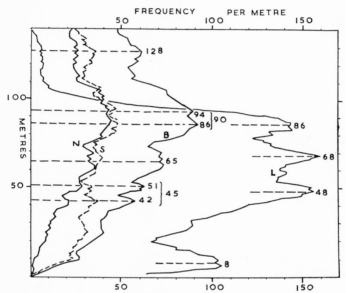

FIG. 34.—Altimetric frequency curves (from spot heights)

B   Peninsular Brittany
N   Northern Peninsular Brittany
S   South Peninsular Brittany
L   Léon

(*After Baulig (re-arranged)*)

the evidence of such contour maps as are available, but hachured maps and those using carefully drawn form-lines at close intervals will often reveal fairly clearly and closely the break of slope. On the 'Relief Only' version of the 5th (Relief) Edition of the O.S. 1-in. map, probably the finest map ever given to the geomorphologist, such features as a plateau facet, a valley-side facet and a valley-bottom facet, may be recognized without difficulty. In general, however, the construction of facet maps involves careful field study and mapping.

Section II. The Analysis of Shape

Patterns of Drainage

Hitherto we have been dealing mainly with the analysis of slope; we may now turn to the analysis of horizontal shape. The pattern of drainage is one of the most revealing features of a landscape and casts light on the rock type, geological structure, stage in drainage evolution, &c. The 'water and contours' print from Ordnance Survey maps, now obtainable through the Geographical Association, is an invaluable aid, but if this is not available, it is an indispensable exercise in the analysis of the relief of an area to trace (or to re-draw by squares) the 'blue' print (i.e. the water).

There is a hierarchy of rivers beginning humbly with headstreams (1st Series) which unite to form a larger stream (2nd Series), many of which may contribute to a large tributary (3rd Series) to a main river (4th Series) reaching the sea. There may, of course, be many more series than this. The relationship of streams of different series are significant as regards (1) their arrangement, which may be dentritic (Gt. Ouse or Upper Shannon), trellised (Medway or Blackwater, Ireland), or in some other pattern produced by adaptation to structure or by superimposition; (2) the relative proportion of each series in number or length. The Kennet, the Nile, and the Colorado have a high proportion of trunk to tributary, the Yorkshire Ouse, the Congo, and the Amazon have a high proportion of tributary to trunk. This leads to a consideration of the hydrographic network.

Hydrographic Network and Texture of Dissection (Geological control)

Ex. A tracing of the drainage pattern from a map that includes both chalk and clay terrain immediately emphasizes the fundamental contrast in their drainage networks—few (but large) artery streams on the chalk carving out wide inter-stream blocks, a fine vein-like pattern dissecting the clay into small inter-stream spaces no part of which is far from a stream or ditch.

Ex. The contrast can be expressed quantitatively in several ways: (1) length of water courses per unit area, (2) number of streams per unit area, (3) number of confluences per unit area. Adopting No. 1, the analytical procedure would be (1) divide the map into squares of about 1-in. side and draw a duplicate set of squares on plain paper. (2) Measure the length of all water courses in each square and set down the total length in the centre of the square on the duplicate. (3) Draw isopleth lines at suitable intervals enclosing similar totals.

The ratio $\dfrac{\text{water length}}{\text{area}}$ may be used as an index of the *texture of drainage*. This is not quite the same thing as the texture of dissection; for example chalk and limestone terrain are much dissected by dry valleys. To express the texture of dissection we must use not the water course but the valley bottoms (thalwegs) whether wet or dry. The ratio $\dfrac{\text{thalweg length}}{\text{area}}$ may be used as an index of the *texture of dissection*.

On the assumption that the dry valleys were once water-cut the index $\dfrac{\text{thalweg length}}{\text{water length}}$ gives a measure of the decline of the water table; an index, as it were, of the degree of drying up.

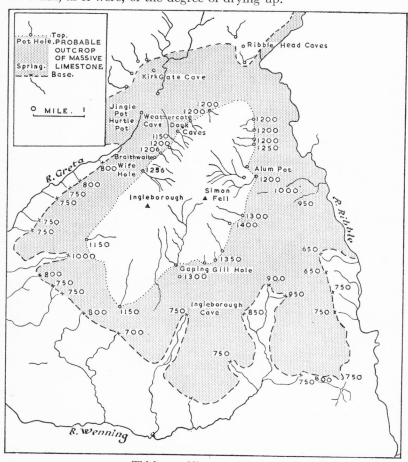

FIG. 35.—Thickness of limestone. Karstic drainage

Patterns of Drainage on Limestones

The extreme case of a coarse texture of dissection is found in areas of thick and massive limestone. Good examples of this 'Karstic' type of scenery are to be found in the Causses on the southern border of the Massif Central. On English maps the best examples are to be found in the Derbyshire and Yorkshire Pennines, and, more compactly, in the Mendip Hills.

Ex. The top of the limestone may often be located approximately by joining the swallow holes, and the base by joining the springs. On

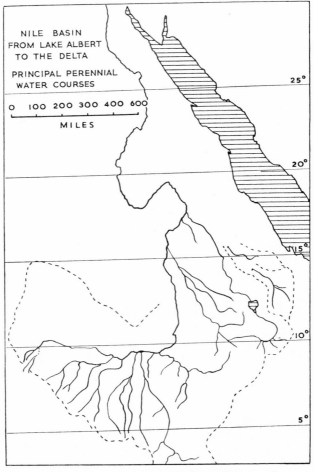

FIG. 36.—Climatic control of hydrographic network

Fig. 35 the limestone appears to be about 500 ft. thick. In applying this simple and rather ingenuous method difficulties are introduced by considerable dips or by the presence of an impervious cover of drift, with or without peat; the geological (drift edition) map is a necessary corrective.

Hydrographic Network (climatic control)

The ratio of the total length of tributaries to the length of trunk may reflect the geological texture (porosity) of the rocks over which the rivers flow; examples of this have been given above. It may also reflect the climatic conditions of the basin. The map of the Nile basin (Fig. 36) provides a simple if rather obvious case, although on such a small scale only the major tributaries can be shown.

Ex. Measure the lengths and calculate the ratio for each reach of 5° of latitude, and compare with the annual rainfall map.

Ex. In order to eliminate the geological factor it is best to select areas similar in geology but contrasted in rainfall and/or evaporation, e.g. the Lombardy Plain with the Hungarian Plain, the Dakota Prairies with the Staked Plains, the Maroccan Meseta with Brittany, &c.

The Pattern of Divides

This is often of equal significance to the pattern of drainage, and like it, consists of (1) primary divides, like the backbone of England, separating rivers flowing to the east and west coasts, (2) secondary divides separating rivers flowing independently to the sea, and (3) tertiary divides separating tributaries from tributaries. They may profitably be drawn in on the drainage map (or tracing) as branching lines running along the crests of ridge and spur, never crossing a river (Fig. 37). They should be drawn in red or some other colour to

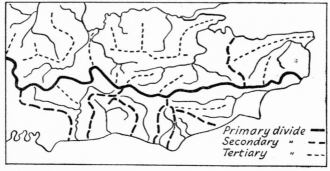

FIG. 37.—The hierarchy of divides in south-east England

distinguish them clearly from the drainage lines with which they will interdigitate. Their pattern is, of course, related to that of the rivers, parallel rivers have parallel divides (e.g. Blackwater, Lee, and Bandon), radial rivers have radial divides (Lake District) and dendritic rivers have dendritic divides.

Ex. The rivers of Southern Ireland may be taken as a good example of a system in which 'adaptation to structure' has proceeded to an extreme degree. The initial drainage of this area (extended consequents flowing across an emerged shore plain) was from north to south, and the secondary divides between the initial consequents must at this stage have run southwards like the prongs of a rake from some primary divide parallel to the south coast. As the 'subsequent' streams grew by encroachment along soft outcrops and capture of neighbouring 'consequents', so the divide gradually shifted to the outcrops of the hard rocks.

At each capture a wind-gap was left high and dry on the hard-rock ridge. From a study of the height of these wind-gaps the order of captures can be deduced and the successive stages in the re-integration of the drainage system reconstructed (see Fig. 38).

In Southern England the process has not gone so far and the chalk outcrop is still breached by the Thames, the only survivor of numerous consequents. A divide line thus runs along the chalk from the Devonshire coast to Streatley and another from Goring to the Wash at Hunstanton; the narrow breach on the divide is as suggestive as the narrow gap through which the river flows.

Ex. The divide pattern of the following areas will repay careful attention. Primary, secondary and tertiary divides should be carefully drawn, the obvious wind-gaps marked in and their summit levels recorded, as on Fig. 38.

> The Weald (Fig. 37).
> The Hampshire Basin and the Isle of Wight.
> The Trent Basin.
> The South-West Peninsula.
> Wales.
> The Pennines.
> The Southern Uplands.

Block Diagrams

The block diagram contributes nothing to the analysis of relief, for it can show nothing more than the map from which it is derived, but as a means of portraying land forms with clarity and for demonstrating the relation between structure and surface it is unrivalled. Everybody who is concerned with the teaching of geography and especially of

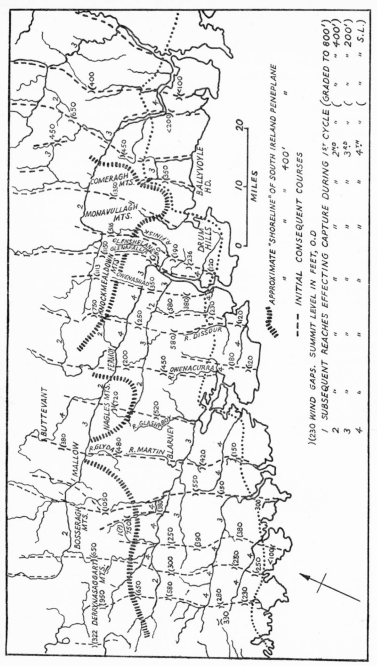

FIG. 38.—Divides, gaps, and captures, Southern Ireland

physiography should strive to make himself as proficient as his skill in draughtsmanship permits in a technique that yielded such excellent results in the hands of W. M. Davis and A. K. Lobeck. The construction of really convincing block diagrams no doubt requires a high degree of technical skill, but there are certain rules and principles that may be learnt and practised which will enable anybody to draw the simpler diagrams quite effectively. A full description of these methods is given by A. K. Lobeck in his book *Block Diagrams*, and his *Geomorphology* contains some hundreds of examples. For those with no artistic gift the purely mechanical Block-Drafter devised by M. Pierre-Th. Dufour and described by Griffith Taylor[1] may be recommended, but much better results are obtained by using a perspective rather than an isometric projection and by using signs and symbols other than form-lines.

The block diagram need not, and in fact cannot, be quantitatively correct as to vertical and horizontal scale, and since its function is demonstration it should be as realistic and convincing as possible. Therefore, since it is designed to convey an impression of landscape to the eye it should be in perspective as seen by the eye. The perspective used may be one-point or two-point as shown in Figs. 39 and 40. In one-point perspective the front of the block is always parallel with the horizon line. It is a limiting case of the two-point in which the second vanishing point (V.P.) is at infinity to right or left of the observer. It will be noticed that the nearer the block is to the horizon line the more obliquely it appears to be viewed, i.e. the further away it seems to be.

If it is desired to prepare a block diagram to illustrate a particular piece of country shown on the map, the map is first ruled in squares and the top of the block, prepared in perspective, is ruled into lozenges representing these squares of the map on any desired scale. One point perspective is easier since the right-to-left lines are parallel and the illusion of distance is created by their coming closer together at the back of the block. A construction for this is given in Fig. 39; *ABCD* is the map; *ABC'D'* is the perspective block. The fore-and-aft lines converge on the vanishing point. The edges of the block are always vertical and the front of the block is rectangular. The side of the block tapers towards the V.P. The spacing of the right-to-left lines on the block is determined by the intersection, with the edge of the block, of lines drawn from the eye to the appropriate point on the grid drawn on the map.

The construction of a two-point perspective block and grid is rather more complicated, but the effect is better and the extra time and trouble are rewarded. The procedure is as follows (see Fig. 40):

    1. Grid the map, select the viewpoint and lay the grid in the desired attitude with the selected near corner towards you.

[1] Griffith Taylor, *The Block Diagram and its Uses* (Lemberg, 1934), and *The Geographical Laboratory*, Univ. Toronto Press, 1938.

2. Draw the horizon line at any distance above the grid; the nearer the grid is to the horizon line the flatter the view of the surface.
3. Position the eye as desired below the grid.
4. From eye position draw lines parallel to grid sides. Where these intersect the horizon line will be the vanishing points.
5. Draw lines from front corner of grid to V.P.s. These determine the front of the block.
6. Draw lines from eye to R. and L. corners of the grid. Where these cut the lines drawn in 5 are R. and L. corners of the block.
7. Draw lines from R.H. corner of *block* to Left V.P. and from

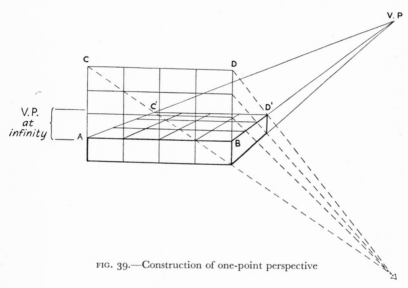

FIG. 39.—Construction of one-point perspective

L.H. corner to Right V.P. Where these lines intersect is the back corner of the block. This point can be fixed by drawing a line from the eye to the far corner of the grid. The surface of the block can now be drawn in.
8. Construct grid on block by joining ends of grid lines on map to eye and marking points of intersection with edges of block.
9. To construct the block sides draw a perpendicular down from the front corner of the block to a suitable depth. Draw lines from the base of this perpendicular to the two V.P.s and drop perpendiculars from R. and L.H. corners of block to these lines. Join the bases of these perpendiculars by lines coming from the V.P.s to form the base of the block.

The next step depends on whether we want to make an accurate

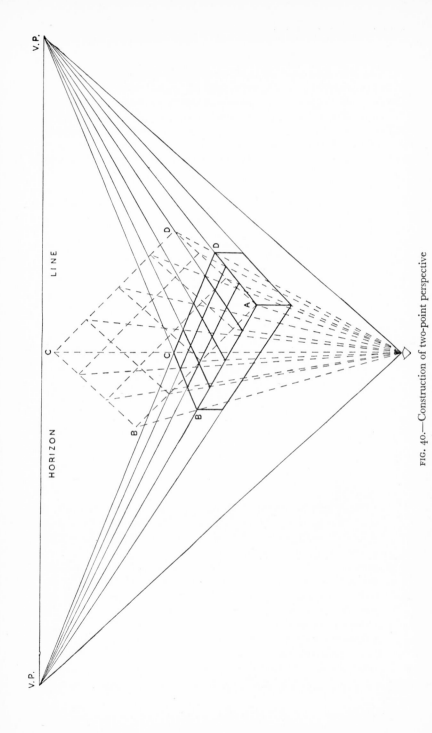

FIG. 40.—Construction of two-point perspective

block diagram or merely a picture of the relief in general terms. Let us take the latter alternative first. The salient features of the map are transferred by means of the squares to their appropriate position on the top of the block, e.g. the rivers and the line of escarpment. The fore-ground, background, and side sections are next drawn in by erecting perpendiculars to scale at each contour, a progressively diminishing scale being used for the background to maintain the proper perspective. The features can now be drawn in conventionally as shown, features

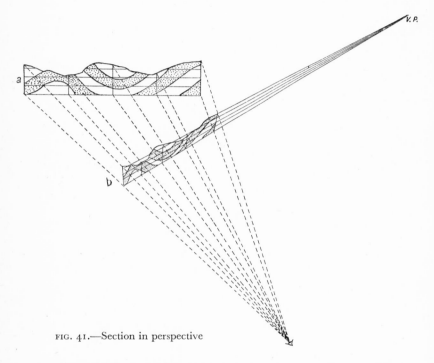

FIG. 41.—Section in perspective

such as loops of rivers, banks, &c. being erased where they are obscured by higher features in front of them.

The geological structure may be inserted in the foreground section to show the relationship between structure and relief, but the rules of perspective must be followed in all but the front of blocks in one point perspective. The section can be gridded and transferred feature by feature to the perspective grid on the side of the block. Thus Fig. 41(a) seen in perspective becomes Fig. 41(b).

If it is desired to prepare a more precise scale diagram each contour must be lifted to its scale altitude. Diagrams of this kind are best done in isometric projection which rather spoils their effectiveness; but complicated and laborious allowances for changing scale are incurred if a perspective projection is used.

The contour map is squared as before and then transferred to the lozenges of the perspective grid. A suitable vertical interval is now selected and the sections of the four sides of the parallelogram are erected on the edges of the block. Each contour in turn is now 'lifted' to its appropriate height. This is best done on tracing paper which is shifted upwards by '100 ft.' for each contour. It will be found, of course, that contours now intersect, which means that foreground is hiding background; the background contours thus hidden should be omitted. Similarly rivers and other low-lying features may be hidden in places by hills in front of them. These too should be omitted. We now have a relief diagram with 'form-lines' which is accurate, though it appears slightly unreal because of the isometric projection.

The Representation of Detail on Block Diagrams

The following principles will act as guides to the attainment of effect:

Horizontal surfaces should be left white or be shaded with short horizontal lines.

Shading on slopes should be in the nature of hachures, i.e. drawn down the direction of steepest slope.

Extra sharpness can be given to cliff edges, &c. by defining with a thin full line.

Shadow effect may be used by shading consistently more heavily on one side of features than on the other, thus giving the impression of illumination from, say, the north-west.

The perspective effect may be enhanced by the insertion of houses, trees, &c. to scale, relatively large in the foreground, decreasing in size with remoteness. They must, however, always be drawn small and with very fine lines.

Fig. 42 shows a few commonly occurring physiographic forms to serve as models.

Valley with interlocking spurs (1).
Glaciated valley (2).
Dissected plateau (3).
Cliff and sandspit (4).
Escarpment with wind-gap (5).
Glaciated mountains (6).
River terraces (7).
                    and some more.

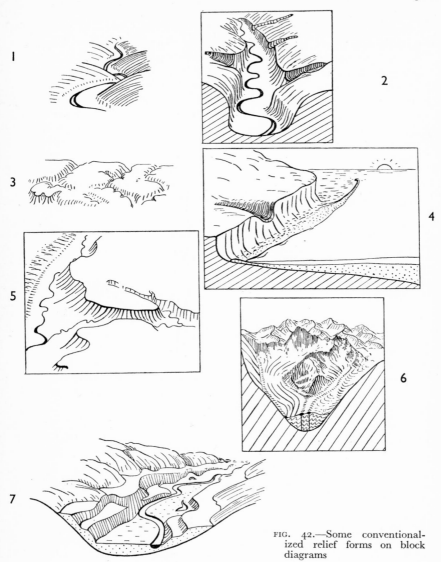

FIG. 42.—Some conventionalized relief forms on block diagrams

Landscape Drawing

This book is concerned only with laboratory exercises, but every student of physiography should try his hand at field sketching, even if the limitations of his skill enable him to record on paper nothing more than the physiographic essentials of a landscape. If he has had no previous training or experience he may discover his gifts or his limitations by trying a freehand sketch from nature; he will probably make grotesque errors in perspective and scale, and will almost certainly make the picture much too high, over-emphasizing vertical at the expense of horizontal lines. To restore his confidence he should then attempt the same landscape using guiding lines and a sketching frame as shown in the illustration (Fig. 43), when it will be found quite easy to produce a fairly convincing and recognizable picture. The same general guiding principles that were used in block diagrams should be remembered, especially the use of a diminishing scale for background features such as trees, buildings, &c. which, being of familiar size, readily convey to the eye the impression of distance.

The physiographer's object in landscape drawing is not simply to

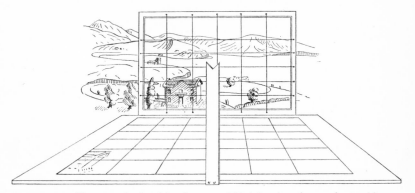

FIG. 43.—Home-made sketching frame and V-sight pinned to a plane table

produce a picture but to examine and describe the significance of its morphology. With this end in view it is permissible and even desirable to omit certain irrelevant features that may have the effect of obscuring the lines and the groupings of forms. Thus hedges, woods, or roads may mask breaks of slope whose presence and position reveal the physiographic build, and the interpretation of the landscape is clearer without them.

Physiographic analysis by landscape drawing is essentially field work and the best results and the most useful exercises are obtained in this way. But the individual may not have the advantage of access to any great variety of physiographic types, for he may live and work in towns or in unsuitable country. If he is deprived of facilities for outdoor work he may still derive valuable exercise by making use of photographs and book illustrations. It is an informative preliminary exercise to trace pictures of, say, mountain valleys and peaks, for in the process he will be impressed with the run of the lines and with the relationships between foreground and background and the overlapping and obscuring of some features by others. Later he can proceed to freehand copying and to idealization and simplification of the landscape.

The Synthesis

In the foregoing pages various devices have been described for examining single qualities of the relief, each taken out of its context and considered independently of the others. In turn we have examined:

1. The geological structure and texture.
2. The vertical distribution of relief—
   a. in valley floors;
   b. in valley sides;
   c. on interfluves and crests.
3. The horizontal distribution of relief—
   a. patterns of rivers;
   b. patterns of interfluves and divides.

All this has been done with a view to discovering evidence bearing on the physiographic evolution of a region. Following this analysis of the parts comes the synthesis of the whole and the formulation of a consecutive evolutionary history which must be compatible with, and based upon, all the evidence gathered together. It would be foolish to claim that this can be done from map analysis alone, for map analysis is only a preliminary to field study. But at least we can formulate hypotheses and check each one against the evidence obtained. Some that appear plausible from the horizontal pattern may be found to carry implications that are contradicted by the valley sections; others suggested by geological distributions may be found to be incompatible with valley shape. It cannot be too strongly emphasized that there is only one right and complete explanation, though the evidence on which it can be reconstructed may not be available. Conversely if any part of the evidence cannot be reconciled with a particular hypothesis, that hypothesis, in the form in which it is held, is wrong.

PART II

THE CIRCULATORY SYSTEMS

CHAPTER 4

THE AIR: ITS MOVEMENT AND PHYSICAL STATE

Section I. The Daily Round. Weather Maps and Diagrams

THE skin of the earth is worn, cracked, and weather-beaten by the sun, the wind, the ice, and the rain of millions of years. The surface layers, exposed to the atmosphere, are slowly worn away and deeper-lying layers are laid bare by erosion; or it may be that a cover of new skin is laid by deposition on parts that lie submerged beneath the sea. Its morphology undergoes a series of evolutionary stages, but at any moment of time it reflects the underlying anatomical structure and, to the discerning eye, its age and its life history are written in its face. Thus the skin of the earth constantly changes and renews itself, and, like the skin and lungs of an animal, takes in air and moisture, uses or wastes them and passes them out again. It is warmed by the fire of the sun, cooled by the winds that blow over its surface, and draws on its reserved of inner heat stored in and below the skin.

Bare and unprotected in the deserts or where man has ploughed and stripped the surface, it lies at the mercy of the elements; in the 'ice deserts' of high latitudes and high altitudes it is clad in a mantle of ice and snow. But in most places it is, in a greater or less degree, protected and clothed with a cover of trees or grass, living things that grow and breathe. Although the individuals die and decay they are replaced by new births, and life goes on, each organism a separate unit reacting to climate and influencing climate in return.

This exchange of heat and moisture across the contact layer between the air and the ground is exceedingly complex. The state of the atmosphere, defined by its temperature, humidity, and all its other qualities, represents the donor, the nature of the earth's surface represents the recipient; the result is the climate. The role of the recipient is not passive; in local detail the composition, texture, and colour of the ground and of its covering of trees, grass, crops, or buildings powerfully affect the rate and direction of exchange; this is the field of micro-climatology. On a larger scale the responses of land and sea to the conditions of the atmosphere are of the greater significance in determining the wider features of climate.

To unravel the tangle of cause and effect, action, reaction, and interaction, calls for patience and care. In nature they are intimately interwoven, and in a description of the total environment all the

CODE FIGURES AND SYMBOLS USED ON WEATHER MAPS

STATION MODEL

Form of High Cloud

Form of Medium Cloud

Dry-Bulb Temperature

Present Weather

Visibility

Dew-Point

Form of Low Cloud

Total Cloud Amount

Wind Direction and Force

Barometric Pressure

Barometric Tendency

Weather in past hour

Past Weather

Amount of Cloud

Height of Cloud

48   17·7   +26
40
44   4/25
40

SYMBOLS FOR FORM OF CLOUD

Code Fig.	Low Cloud	Medium Cloud
1	Cu—little developed	As—thin
2	Cu—much developed	As—thick, or Ns
3	Cb—without anvil	Ac—thin
4	Sc—from spreading of Cu	Ac—thin in patches
5	Sc—not from Cu	Ac—thin, in bands increasing
6	St or Fs—not under Ns	Ac—from spreading of Cu
7	Fs ('Scud')—under Ns	Ac—with As, or thick Ac—not increasing
8	Cu and Sc	Ac—castellatus
9	Cb—with anvil	Ac—several layers chaotic sky

Code Fig.	High Cloud
1	Ci—fine, not increasing
2	Ci—dense, not increasing
3	Ci—anvil-shaped
4	Ci—fine, increasing
5	Ci and Cs—distant, increasing
6	Ci and Cs—closer, increasing
7	Cs—continuous, covering whole sky
8	Cs—not continuous, not increasing
9	Cc—alone or with Ci or Cs

TOTAL CLOUD AMOUNT—in oktas (eighths) of sky covered

○	⊖	①	⊕	⑪
None	1 or trace	2	3	4

⊕	⑪	⑪	⑪	⊗
5	6	7 or overcast with openings	8	Sky obscured

AMOUNT OF LOW CLOUD—in oktas, as above

HEIGHT OF LOW CLOUD—in 1-figure or 2-figure codes

ONE-FIGURE CODE

Code Fig.		Height of Cloud Base (ft.)
0	. . . . . .	0– 150
1	. . . . . .	150– 300
2	. . . . . .	300– 600
3	. . . . . .	600–1000
4	. . . . . .	1000–2000
5	. . . . . .	2000–3000
6	. . . . . .	3000–5000
7	. . . . . .	5000–6500
8	. . . . . .	6500–8000
9	. . . . . .	above 8000

TWO-FIGURE CODE

From 01 to 80 code figure = height of cloud in hundreds of feet.

E.g.
00 = < 100 ft.
01 = 100 ft.
02 = 200 ft.
79 = 7900 ft.
80 = 8000 ft.

Figures 90–99 used when heights cannot be determined with greater accuracy, they are equivalent to 1-figure code 0–9.

WIND

Beaufort number	knots	Force: m.p.h.	Symbol
0	< 1	1	◎
1	1–3	1–3	
2	4–6	4–7	
3	7–10	8–12	
4	11–16	13–18	
5	17–21	19–24	
6	22–27	25–31	
7	28–33	32–38	
8	34–40	39–46	
9	41–47	47–54	
10	48–55	55–63	

Gustiness

WEATHER SYMBOLS AND BEAUFORT LETTERS (SELECTION)

PRESENT WEATHER

APPEARANCE OF SKY—no symbols used: b—blue sky ($<$ $\frac{1}{4}$ covered): bc—$\frac{1}{4}$ to $\frac{3}{4}$ covered: c—cloudy ($>$ $\frac{3}{4}$ covered) but with openings: o—overcast (continuous sheet): g—gloom.

	Thinning. last hour	No change	Thickening, last hour
FOG (f) ☰ Fog, sky discernible	☰|	☰	|☰
In patches. Thick Fog.	☰|	☰	|☰

HAZE (z) ∞ MIST (m) ═

PRECIPITATION—capital letter signifies Heavy   e.g. R
            small letter   ,,   Moderate   e.g. r
            suffix o   ,,   Slight   e.g. r_0
            prefix i   ,,   Intermittent   e.g. ir
            doubling letter   ,,   Continuous   e.g. rr

	Light Intermittent	Light Continuous	Moderate Intermittent	Moderate Continuous	Heavy Intermittent	Heavy Continuous
DRIZZLE (d)	,	, ,	⁏	, ,	⁏	, , ,
RAIN (r)	●	● ●	⦂	● ●	⁞	●● ●
SNOW (s)	✱	✱ ✱	✱ ✱	✱ ✱	✱✱✱	✱✱✱

SLEET ✻   DEW (w)   Hoar-Frost (x) } no symbol used

SHOWERS (p) Slight ∇̇   Heavy ∇̇   Violent ∇̇   Snow ∇   Hail (h) ◮◮◮

THUNDERSTORMS (tl) Slight or Moderate ↙   Heavy ↙   With Rain/Snow ↙

With Hail ↙

PAST WEATHER

◯	⦸	⦷	☰	●
Fair	Variable sky	Overcast	Fog	Drizzle

●	✱	∇	↙
Rain	Snow or sleet	Showers	Thunderstorm

DRY-BULB TEMPERATURE AND DEW-POINT—in ° F.

BAROMETRIC PRESSURE—in mb—last 3 figures (1 decimal place) only.

BAROMETRIC TENDENCY—in $\frac{1}{10}$ mb ±.

VISIBILITY

X1 = 20 yds.	81 = 12 miles	90 = 0 − 55 yds.
X2 = 40 ,,	82 = 25 ,,	91 = 55 − 220 ,,
by 20 yds. to	83 = 37 ,,	92 = 220 − 550 ,,
X9 = 180 yds.	84 = 50 ,,	93 = 550 −1100 ,,
01 = $\frac{1}{8}$ mile	85 = 62 ,,	94 = 1100 −2200 ,,
02 = $\frac{1}{4}$,,	86 = 93 ,,	95 = $1\frac{1}{4}$− $2\frac{1}{2}$,,
03 = $\frac{3}{8}$,,	87 = 125 ,,	96 = $2\frac{1}{2}$− $6\frac{1}{4}$,,
by $\frac{1}{8}$ mile to	88 = 187 ,,	97 = $6\frac{1}{4}$− $12\frac{1}{2}$,,
80 = 10 miles	89 = > 310 ,,	98 = $12\frac{1}{2}$− 31 ,,
		99 = > 31 ,,

Figures 90–99 used when visibility cannot be determined with greater accuracy: they are equivalent to old code 0–9.

FRONTS

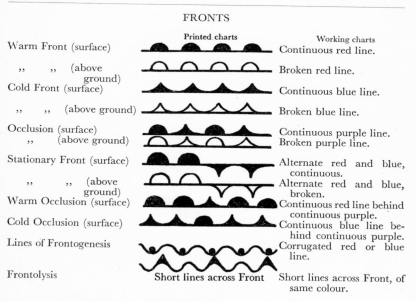

	Printed charts	Working charts
Warm Front (surface)		Continuous red line.
,, ,, (above ground)		Broken red line.
Cold Front (surface)		Continuous blue line.
,, ,, (above ground)		Broken blue line.
Occlusion (surface)		Continuous purple line.
,, (above ground)		Broken purple line.
Stationary Front (surface)		Alternate red and blue, continuous.
,, ,, (above ground)		Alternate red and blue, broken.
Warm Occlusion (surface)		Continuous red line behind continuous purple.
Cold Occlusion (surface)		Continuous blue line behind continuous purple.
Lines of Frontogenesis		Corrugated red or blue line.
Frontolysis	Short lines across Front	Short lines across Front, of same colour.

Note: symbols are placed on that side of line towards which Front is moving.

component parts must be given their due weight. The device that comes nearest to this desirable aim is the 'synoptic chart' that shows at any moment of time the totality of weather, though not of climate. Such a map, like all maps, is a synthesis; its understanding demands analysis. So, as with other maps, we may take it apart and examine its texture, strand by strand. But first let us examine the overall picture given by the synoptic chart.

The Pattern and Design of Weather Maps

Wind and weather know no frontiers and pass from kingdom to republic without let or leave; weather science must, therefore, be international in outlook and demands international agreement on the signs and symbols to be used. There is a general similarity between most of the national weather maps, and when one has been carefully studied the rest can be fairly easily understood. The *Daily Weather Report*[1] of the Meteorological Office, London, will serve as an example and as a source of data for exercises. It is a four-page document; on pp. 1 and 4 it provides, in tabular form, the data recorded at 55 stations in the British Isles at four periods of the day, 12 noon, 6 p.m., 12 midnight, and 6 a.m. G.M.T. The inside pages (2 and 3) are in map form, showing the pressure, temperature, wind, and cloud; isobars are drawn and fronts are shown. The mid-day map (p. 2) shows most of the Northern hemisphere and gives a semi-global picture; the 6 a.m. map is more restricted, it includes Western Europe and the East Atlantic; the 6 p.m. and midnight maps show only the British Isles and the adjacent parts of the Continent. The present series of the *Daily Weather Report* superseded, in January 1949, an earlier one in which p. 2 showed the 6 a.m. conditions over the British Isles and adjacent continental countries on a generous scale of 1/5 M. This was an excellent teaching map because it used the 'Station Model' by which all the elements of the weather, conventionally represented, were shown grouped round the position of each station. The total assemblage of information offered an excellent opportunity for the exercise of the supreme faculty of the map reader, the power of visualizing all the elements of the situation presented synoptically by conventional signs. It is a great pity that the *Daily Weather Report* no longer supplies, for the serious student of Meteorology, this indispensable instrument. In forecasting practice the station model is always used, and the student of meteorology must make himself familiar with its construction.

A typical station model, with explanation, is shown on p. 92, and there is no better way of acquiring familiarity with its use than to construct a few dozen, using the data on pp. 1 and 4 of the present

[1] Obtainable from The Director, Meteorological Office, Air Ministry, Kingsway, London, W.C.2. Subscription rate 2d. per copy, or 3d. post free: there are special arrangements for schools and colleges.

series *Weather Report* and the various code figures and symbols shown on pages 92–95 of this book. Apart from one or two slight amendments introduced recently these are the same specifications and symbols that were used on the former charts (though no key was provided with them).

Ex. On the map (Fig. 44) the position of a number of stations is shown and the data for these stations are provided for 6 a.m. on April 9th, 1951, in column form below. The data for Kew are plotted on a modified form of station model. The reader may plot the remainder for practice.

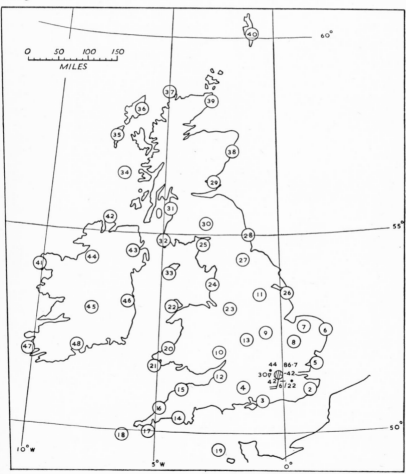

FIG. 44.—Weather observation stations. Kew model plotted

TABLE 4: *Observations at 06 hr. G.M.T., 9th April 1951.*

	Stations	Height above M.S.L.	Wind Direction (degrees) [17]	Wind Speed (kts.) [18]	Visibility [19]	Present weather [20]	Pressure Bar. at M.S.L. [21]	Pressure Change in 3 hrs. [22]	Temp. Dry bulb [23]	Temp. Dew-point [24]	Form Low [25]	Form Medium [26]	Form High [27]	Cloud Total amt. [28]	Cloud Main layer Amt. [29]	Cloud Main layer [30]	Cloud Lowest layer Amt. [31]	Cloud Lowest layer [32]	State of ground [33]	Weather 21 h. to 03 h. [39]	Weather 03 h. to 09 h. [40]
1	Kew	18	190	12	30	pr_0	86.7	−42	44	42	6			7	6	22			1	$ccr_0r_0RRm_0$	crr_0ccpr_0
2	Lympne	341	190	17	20	r_0r_0	90.5	−43	43	42	7	2		8	8	06	3	03	2	cir_0	$or_0r_0pr_0$
3	Tangmere	53	210	17	40	cr	87.7	−47	45	43	8	3		7	3	15	4	17	1	$cr_0r_0m_0$	$crrm_0cir_0$
4	Boscombe Down	414	230	15	72	o	85.7	−42	42	39	5			8	8	12	1		1	$crrr_0r_0$	$cd_0d_0id_0$
5	Felixstowe	10	160	19	44	r_0r_0	89.8	−33	44	43	6	7		8	7	75	5	17	2	ccr_0r_0	cr_0r_0crrc
6	Gorleston	5	280	08	32	ir_0	91.0	−25	42	40	7	2		8	8		7	09	2	ccm_0om_0	$orrm_0$
7	West Raynham	250	160	10	32	r_0r_0	89.4	−27	41	40	7			8	8	25			2	$ccrrr_0r_0c$	$bccir_0rrm_0$
8	Mildenhall	15	160	11	48	r_0r_0	87.6	−35	42	40	7	2		8	8	25	3	12	2	$cirm_0cRR$	$or_0r_0cr_0r_0$
9	Cottesmore	452	080	05	24	r_0r_0	87.4	−29	39	39	5			8	8	10			2	cr_0mcm_0	om_0orr
10	Ross-on-Wye	223	340	01	34	ps_0	86.3	−20	36	35		2		8	8	10			2	ccr	rr
11	Finningley	52	050	05	13	o	88.6	−17	39	38	5			8	5	25			1	$crrcm_0$	cm_0c
12	Bristol	209	320	06	32	d_0d_0	85.2	−26	39	38	6			8	8	15	7	08	2	r_0r_0rr	$rrRRd_0r_0$
13	Elmdon	326																	2	$cbcid$	$cidRRrr$
14	Plymouth	90	290	14	80	bc	91.1	+13	42	38	9			4	4	10			2	$cRRm_0cm_0$	cir_0m_0cpr
15	Chivenor	20	340	23	80	rr	89.8	+22	39	38		2		8	8	15	1	10	2	cr_0phpr	cir_0ccpr_0
16	St. Eval	336	300	14	72	pr_0	92.9	+09	39	36	3			7	7	18			2	cRm_0rrir_0c	cir_0phrpr_0
17	Lizard	240	290	12	80	bc	94.3	−18	43	39	3			3	3	18			1	$bcprq$	$bcpr$
18	Scilly, St. Mary's	163	310	23	81	c	93.7	+05	43	38	8			6	6	12	3		1	$oircprc$	$cbcpr$
19	Guernsey	340	290	24	81	bc	92.9	−08	43	38	3	4		5	3	20	4	12	1	$bccrirc$	$circbcpr_0$
20	Aberporth	375	280	10	81	c	89.3	−15	42	38	8			7	4	25		10	2	$ccpr_0ir_0$	cir_0c

No	Station																				
21	St. Ann's Head	142	320	14	81	c	90.3	+06	42	38	3	7	—	6	5	17	—	—	2	$crrbccpr_0$	c
22	Holyhead (Valley)	32	020	12	64	od	90.3	+10	40	38	5	—	—	8	8	18	2	08	1	bcbbc	$bcdid_0bc$
23	Manchester	230	050	10	16	c	89.3	−08	38	37	5	—	—	8	6	10	—	—	—	$cir_0cr_0r_0$	c
24	Squires Gate	33	020	11	80	b	90.2	−03	39	35	5	—	—	7	7	25	—	—	1	$cr_0r_0vd_0d_0$	cm_0
25	Silloth	25	020	09	64	b	92.9	+04	33	31	—	7	—	1	1	—	—	—	1	bm_0bx	$bxbm_0b$
26	Spurn Head	29	090	06	32	c	89.9	−21	41	40	3	—	—	7	3	25	4	20	1	or_0r_0	c
27	Leeming	105	020	10	12	r_0r_0	91.0	−09	36	35	7	2	—	8	8	22	3	10	2	bcrr	$crrcm_0ir_0$
28	Tynemouth	108	340	13	16	pr_0	92.4	−06	38	37	8	—	—	7	7	20	—	—	2	bm_0cm_0	$cm_0cpr_0m_0$
29	Leuchars	36	290	03	81	bc	94.4	+04	32	27	—	3	5	4	3	81	—	—	1	b	bcpsc
30	Eskdalemuir	794	350	08	81	b	93.2	−04	29	26	5	—	—	1	1	50	—	—	1	bx	bxbx
31	Prestwick	30	150	02	24	b	95.0	+09	29	26	—	4	1	1	—	—	—	—	0	bwbwmbx	bxcbcwm
32	West Freugh	52	020	05	64	b	93.9	+05	34	31	—	4	—	—	1	81	—	—	1	bwbx	bx
33	Ronaldsway	55	010	12	81	cpr	92.8	+04	37	31	5	3	1	2	2	40	—	—	1	cr_0r_0bc	bcb
34	Tiree	29	010	20	82	bc	96.8	+09	41	33	8	3	2	6	1	30	2	18	0	bv	$bbccpr_0bc$
35	Benbecula	16	020	14	82	bc	98.8	+19	37	34	2	3	.	3	2	20	—	—	1	$bbxpr_0b$	$bcpr_0bc$
36	Stornoway	10	360	16	81	bc	95.5	+20	37	34	3	—	—	3	3	24	—	—	2	$bcpr_0$	$bcpr_0$
37	Cape Wrath	367	360	19	82	c	96.7	+08	38	35	5	—	—	7	7	20	—	—	1	cpr	cpr
38	Dyce	234	270	10	80	cps	93.5	+01	35	38	9	—	—	7	6	20	3	12	2	bx	$bcxcpr_0sprsc$
39	Wick	119	350	17	81	c	94.1	+15	38	36	2	7	—	7	5	18	—	—	2	cprs	prc
40	Lerwick	269	010	08	82	or	93.9	+17	37	35	8	—	2	6	5	15	2	17	2	cpr_0	cir_0bcpr_0c
41	Blacksod Point	18	010	07	81	jp	99.3	+22	41	35	9	—	—	5	5	21	—	—	1	pr	pr
42	Malin Head	84	350	05	83	pr_0	97.0	+04	40	34	8	—	—	5	4	36	—	—	2	cpr	pr
43	Aldergrove	220	360	06	82	b	95.5	+13	32	30	8	3	—	1	1	35	1	25	1	$cr_0r_0m_0bcb$	bvbc
44	Castle Archdale	225	330	07	82	bdpr	96.9	+19	34	30	8	—	—	1	1	25	—	—	1	cid_0c	cpr_0bxcir_0
45	Birr Castle	187	310	09	81	o	95.2	+29	38	33	5	2	—	8	6	40	—	—	1	b	r
46	Collinstown	226	330	14	81	bc	94.1	+17	37	33	2	3	2	4	1	20	—	—	1	pr	r
47	Valentia	30	010	12	81	cpr	98.2	+21	40	36	3	—	—	7	7	21	—	—	1	pr	pr
48	Midleton	30	330	15	81	pr_0	95.4	+18	39	35	3	—	—	7	7	21	—	—	1	r	pr

Taking the Weather Map to Pieces

The interpretation of weather maps and the preparation of forecasts demand long practice and experience, and the most successful forecasters are those most willing and able to profit by experience. It is an error to suppose, as we often hear said, that forecasting is something of an 'art', carrying the implication that people are born with the gift. Success depends on a conscious and intelligent analysis of the causes of past successes and failures, by which a store of practical knowledge is accumulated and then applied. The mental processes involved may in time become subconscious, but they are never subjective or unscientific.

In the ordinary way of forecasting, the trained meteorologist takes in, at a glance, the miscellaneous distributions shown round the station model and puts all the evidence together in his head. We may admire this mental process of visualization and synthesis, but we shall only be able to emulate it by devoting to it the hours of practice that he has given. In the meantime we shall probably arrive at an appreciation of the situation more thoroughly, if more slowly, by pulling the station model to pieces and plotting separately those elements that are plottable.

Of these various elements the one of greatest significance is pressure and it is mainly for this reason that it is selected for representation by isopleths (isobars). But there are two other reasons for this preoccupation with pressure and the comparative neglect of the other elements. The first is historical; in the development of synoptic meteorology, the pressure pattern (cyclones, anticyclones, troughs, wedges, &c.) has for long been the fundamental unit and has become thoroughly familiar. But since the work of Bjerknes during the First World War, the 'air mass' has assumed a still more fundamental role. The air mass concept has shed a great flood of light on weather processes, but it seems that our great-grandfathers were familiar with 'the polar and equatorial air currents and the elemental wars to which the confliction gives rise.' [1] For many years this concept, so simple and satisfying in broad outline, was strangled in the noose of isobars.

The full recognition of the significance of air masses led to the appearance on weather maps of lines marking the intersection of their delimiting 'fronts' with the earth's surface. These in no way interfere with the pressure pattern as represented by the isobars, rather they serve to interpret and explain it.

The second reason for selecting pressure for representation by isopleths is that pressure is a continuous distribution, always producing a clear pattern of unbroken transition. The same cannot be said of precipitation, cloud amount, or visibility, whose distributions tend to

[1] See letter to *Weather*, Vol. 5, No. 5, May 1950.

be patchy, with sudden breaks and discontinuities. But temperature is another continuous distribution and it is nearly always possible to construct a rational system of isotherms on a weather map. This has

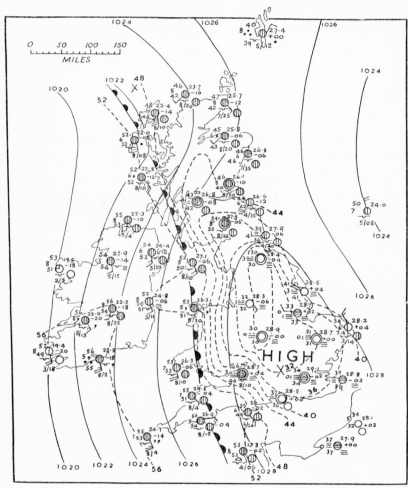

FIG. 45.—Isotherms at 4° F. intervals overdrawn on a weather map

Full lines are isobars, broken lines are isotherms

been done in Fig. 45, which has been selected to show a rather remarkable incursion of warm moist air from the west after a cold spell. The crowding of the isotherms defines the front more clearly than any of the other elements. Such a striking example would, of course, be obvious from a quick inspection of the map, but less spectacular cases, which might otherwise escape notice, may often be detected by the construction of an isothermal map for the day.

Other elements shown on the station model will often be worth plotting separately in the same way, e.g.

1. Barometric change. This gives a clue to the movement of pressure systems.
2. Rain and other forms of precipitation.
3. Dew-point.
4. Visibility.
5. Wind direction.
6. Cloud type, amount, and height.

Their distribution will provide clues for the recognition of air masses and the fronts that separate them.

Ex. Fill in the blanks on Fig. 46 and draw isopleths at suitable intervals. The exercise can be repeated by taking the data from the *Weather Report* on any day when well-contrasted air masses are in occupation of the British Isles and plotting them on an outline map.[1]

Pressure and Wind: the Geostrophic Scale

Guidance as to the relation of wind to pressure can be found in weather manuals and cannot be described here, but it is a curious omission from the weather map that, though it shows scales of distance and millibar-inch equivalents of pressure, it provides no geostrophic scale by which wind velocity can be estimated from the isobar spacing; the scale can also be used for estimating the speed of travel of fronts. (See p. 105.) It is a very useful instrument, but the student can easily make his own on a piece of card by following the simple instructions given below.

Regrettably the scale of the largest map (0600h) on the present series *Weather Report* is too small (1/20 M) for accurate use of the geostrophic scale and the former series (1/5 M) will be used here. Fig. 47 shows the isobars and wind force and direction on a portion of one of these maps (reproduced to scale) and can be used for practice.

Ex. Mark off along the edge of the card a length of 12 cm. (4·8 in.) and write 5 (m.p.h.) there. Bisect this distance (6 cm.) and write 10. Bisect the left half and write 20. Repeat, doubling the wind velocity for each bisection of the left-hand interval. This will give you a geostrophic wind scale suitable for use on the 1/5 M British Isles map, with an isobar interval of 2 mb.

---

[1] Suitable maps (MO. Form 2216), showing the position of the stations, may be obtained from H.M. Stationery Office. An alternative method is to use tracing paper.

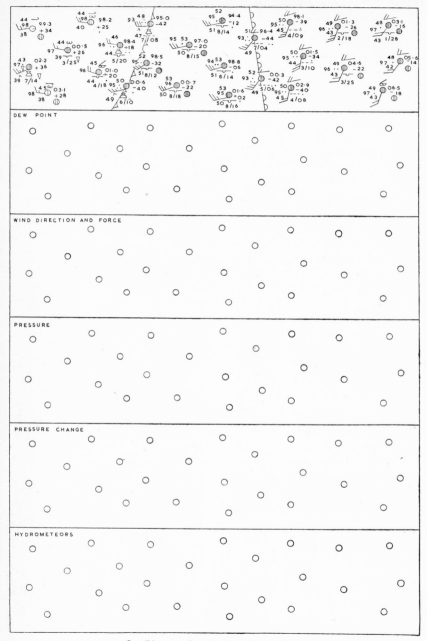

FIG. 46.—Piecemeal analysis of the station model

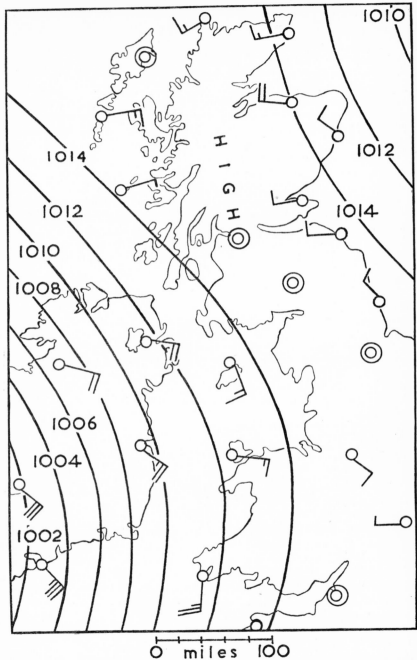

0600h. G.M.T. Tuesday, 25th February 1947

FIG. 47.—Use of geostrophic scale for determining wind velocity

[If in spite of the inaccuracies inevitably incurred it is desired to use the geostrophic scale, on the present series (0600h map, scale 1/20 M) the lengths of each part of the scale would need to be divided by 2, because, though the scale is ¼ (1/20 M) the isobar interval is double (4 mb.)]

The geostrophic wind (reached at about 2,000 ft.) blows parallel to the isobars, and its force can be measured by placing the scale across the isobars at right angles, with its left-hand end on one isobar, and reading off the appropriate velocity where it cuts the next isobar.

Friction against the ground retards the flow of air. This effect varies considerably with the degree of turbulence of the atmosphere (and therefore with time of day, air mass, &c.), and with the nature of the surface. The retardation of the air flow also causes a deflection, so that, instead of flowing parallel to the isobars, surface winds are inclined to them at a certain angle towards the direction of lower pressure.

Approximate figures showing the relation between surface wind and geostrophic wind in different conditions are given below.

	Surface wind speed as fraction of geostrophic		Angle between surface wind and Isobar	
	Day	Night	Day	Night
Over sea	0·75	0·75	10° or less	10° or less
Over land	0·6	0·25	20°	30° or more

Ex. The student should use his home-made geostrophic scale to estimate the geostrophic wind from the isobars in the neighbourhood of the station models on Fig. 47 or on one of the old series maps, set them down in columns as shown below, and compare them with the surface wind force and direction as given on Fig. 47 or on p. 1 and 4 of the weather map.

	Cork.	Aberdeen.
1. Station.		
2. Wind direction		
3. Isobar direction		
4. Angle between 2 and 3 . . .		
5. Geostrophic wind from scale .		
6. Surface wind force		
7. Difference between 5 and 6 . .		

The Movement of Fronts

In predicting the travel of weather and of fronts with which it is associated the forecaster has the advantage of studying the past behaviour of fronts. The student, from a comparison of two or more consecutive maps, can get some information in this way for himself, but a rough guide to the direction and speed of travel from a single map is provided by the use of the geostrophic scale. The procedure is as follows (see Fig. 48).

Place the geostrophic scale along the front with the end on one isobar and read off the value where it crosses the next. It will be appreciated that this does not give the wind velocity since the scale is not placed at right angles to the isobars, which meet the front at an angle. But it does give approximately the speed of movement of the front at right angles to its length. In Fig. 48, which shows a cold front, the speed is about 18 m.p.h. In six hours' time the front will have moved in the direction shown by the dotted lines, a distance of $18 \times 6 = 108$ miles. With a warm front, the speed of movement is lower, and should be taken as approximately $\frac{3}{4}$ of the geostrophic value. Hence cold fronts generally overtake warm fronts, bringing about occlusion.

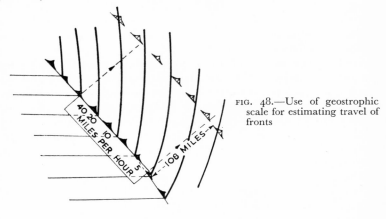

FIG. 48.—Use of geostrophic scale for estimating travel of fronts

Temperature-Height Diagrams

Weather is in three dimensions and we can no more afford to ignore the vertical section of the atmosphere than of the earth's crust. The temperature-height diagram (the 'tephigram' and its variants) is an indispensable tool of the meteorologist and has been skilfully contrived and improved. Any serious and accurate work in meteorology must make use of these devices, and the user must thoroughly understand what they mean. This demands a knowledge of physics and an understanding of mathematical concepts such as not all geography students possess. But at considerable sacrifice of precision and by a high-handed treatment of physical theory we may learn much from the use of simple temperature-height graphs on rectangular co-ordinates, using arithmetical (not logarithmic) scales (i.e. on ordinary graph paper). On tephigrams the lines of equal pressure, temperature (except dry adiabats), and humidity are all curved, so the framework of the graph cannot be home-made, but on the simple form used here three of the essential lines, i.e. temperature, height, and dry adiabats, are straight; no difficulty will be experienced until the subject of 'saturated adiabats' arises, when recourse must be had to an approximation, and, even then, the lines must unfortunately be curved, as will be explained below.

Abundant statistical material for temperature-height analysis can be obtained from the *Daily Aerological Record* of the Meteorological Office, London. This, in its present form, is a six-page publication including, quite apart from charts and notes on the aerological situation, radio-soundings of temperature, humidity, and wind speed and direction for nine land stations and a number of ships, made at four standard times every day.

The simplified form of temperature-height diagram, suitable for the plotting of these 'ascents', is shown in Fig. 49. The inclusion of 'dry' and 'saturated adiabats' increases the scope of the diagram, making possible a number of exercises which throw light particularly on the mechanism of convectional activity.

When dry, i.e. non-saturated, air ascends (or descends) in the free atmosphere, it cools (or warms up) at a constant rate of 5·4° F. per 1,000 ft. This is known as the dry adiabatic lapse rate (D.A.L.R.), and can be depicted on the diagram as a line of constant slope, or 'dry adiabat'. The broken lines in Fig. 49 are dry adiabats, and so are any other lines drawn parallel to them. The path of all such lines represents the temperature changes in ascending or descending bodies of unsaturated air.

When air becomes saturated, a new factor enters the situation—that of condensation. The consequent liberation of latent heat reduces the rate at which rising air cools, and a new lapse rate is established for saturated air. The saturated adiabatic lapse rate (S.A.L.R.), unlike the D.A.L.R., is not constant, but varies with the air temperature. At relatively high temperatures, the S.A.L.R. is about half the D.A.L.R.: at low temperatures, with less water vapour present to condense, and consequently less latent heat to liberate, the two lapse rates are practically the same. Thus, on the diagram, the 'saturated adiabats' are curves (dotted), steeper than the dry adiabats in the lower layers, and becoming parallel to them at great heights. (These curves are derived from those of the tephigram, by an approximate method.) All such curves represent the temperature changes in ascending or descending saturated air.

Vertical temperature lines, horizontal height lines, dry and saturated adiabats provide the essential framework of our temperature-height diagram. Against this are plotted the data of the radio-sounding. Fig. 49 shows a sample ascent (continuous line). This depicts the actual condition of the atmosphere above the given station, and at the given time. The actual change of temperature with height, as recorded by the aircraft or sounding balloon, may be called the environment lapse rate (E.L.R.), represented on the diagram by the continuous line of the environment curve.

Against each plotted point on the environment curve is entered a figure, which gives us information regarding the moisture content of

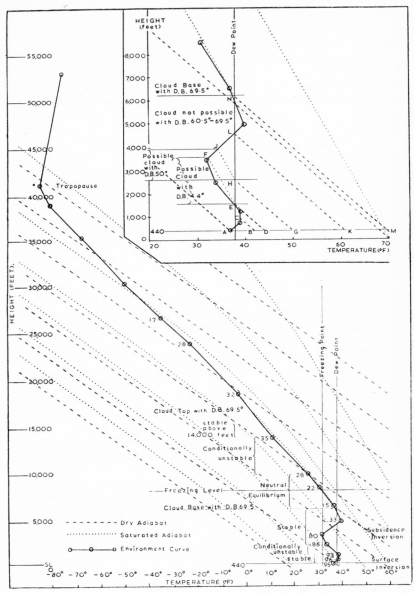

FIG. 49.—Sample ascent plotted on simplified height diagram

the air. In the *Daily Aerological Record*, dew-points are given, and these may be entered on the diagram. Alternatively, the dew-points may be converted to relative humidities (by the use of hygrometric tables) and these entered, as in Fig. 49.

Much of the working with temperature-height diagrams involves the lower layers of the atmosphere, and the untidy confusion of lines will be avoided if we include an inset graph on a larger scale, on which the lowest part of the ascent may be reproduced, as is done on Fig. 49.

Exercises on Temperature-Height Diagrams

The actual exercises which can be carried out with upper-air data necessarily depend on the particular 'ascent' in question. The general form of the exercises, however, will not vary greatly, and the scheme suggested below will cover many of the possibilities.

Ex. 1. Plot the ascent given.
2. Locate and state the height of the tropopause.
3. Determine the average lapse rate within the troposphere.
4. Describe the stability conditions of the air at all heights, locating and explaining any inversions of temperature.
5. Determine the dew-pont of the lowest layers, and draw a vertical dew-point line.
6. Ascertain whether convection cloud is possible at the time of the ascent.
7. If so, determine the condensation level, i.e. cloud base, and cloud top.
8. If not, determine the minimum surface temperature required to produce convection cloud.
9. Determine cloud base and top for the condition of 8.
10. Assume late morning or afternoon rises of surface temperature of (e.g.) 5° and 10°, and determine the base and top of convection cloud (if any) due to these conditions.
11. Find the freezing level (F.L.).
12. Determine the minimum surface temperature required to produce cloud top above F.L.
13. Determine the minimum surface temperature required to produce a cloud thickness of 10,000 ft. or more.
14. Discuss the possibilities of showers and/or thunderstorms, in the light of the above information.
15. Determine cloud base and top (if any) for forced ascent.

The procedure for determining each of these fifteen answers is given below.

Discussion of an Example

1. The E.L.R. plotted in Fig. 49 represents an ascent from an inland station at 0600 hours G.M.T. on a winter day.

2. The height of the tropopause is 41,000 ft.

3. The average lapse rate within the troposphere (i.e. between surface and tropopause) is given by a net fall of temperature of $(37 + 85)°$ or $122°$ in nearly 41,000 ft., or $3°$ per 1,000 ft. approximately. The 'surface', for this ascent, is actually 440 ft. above sea-level : this is insignificant for the above calculation, but, for all other determinations, must form the effective base of the graph.

4. Stability conditions on the diagram are governed by the relation of the slope of the environment curve to those of the dry and saturated adiabats. A layer of air for which the environment curve has a steeper slope (i.e. a smaller fall in temperature for a given range of height) than the saturated adiabet passing through it, is stable (E.L.R. < S.A.L.R.). A layer of air for which the environment curve slopes less steeply than the dry adiabat passing through it (i.e. a more rapid fall in temperature with height), is unstable (E.L.R. > D.A.L.R.). If the slope of the environment curve is intermediate between those of the dry and saturated adiabats, the air layer is conditionally unstable (D.A.L.R. > E.L.R. > S.A.L.R.). A portion of the environment curve may lie parallel to either a dry or a saturated adiabat (E.L.R. = D.A.L.R. or S.A.L.R.) exhibiting neutral or indifferent equilibrium. In Fig. 49 the stability conditions of the environment curve are indicated.

Three inversions are shown on this ascent. The highest is the tropopause, at 41,000 ft.: the lowest is a surface inversion, plainly the result of night radiation and cooling. The third is at 3,500 ft., an anticyclonic or subsidence inversion, its nature made evident by the low relative humidities in the air above.

5. The dew-point of any air layer can be found from *Hygrometric Tables* (Meteorological Office, M.O. 265) if the dry bulb temperature and relative humidity are known. The dew-point of the lowest layer is especially important for consideration of the possibilities of convection cloud development. It is generally a late morning or mid-day dew-point that is significant for this purpose, i.e. one that is normally higher than the 0600 hour dew-point given by the ascent (especially under the particular conditions of a surface inversion which will later vanish). If the later dew-point is not known, it must be forecast, and it would be reasonable to accept the dew-point at 1,000 ft. on the 0600 ascent as the required value.

In Fig. 49 the dry-bulb temperature at 1,000 ft. is $39°$, and the relative humidity may be taken as 94 per cent. or 95 per cent. The corresponding dew-point, as found from the Tables, is then $38°$. Since, while the dry-bulb temperature varies dry-adiabatically, the change in dew-point is so small that it can be ignored, a vertical line can now be drawn through $38°$ on the diagram.

6, 7. It will readily be seen that there is no possibility of free convection in this air at the time of the ascent. If on the inset map a dry adiabat is drawn from the base at A, it lies entirely to the left of the environment curve, i.e. rising air would at all times be cooler (and heavier) than its environment, and would therefore tend to sink. This, of course, follows from the stability of the lowest layers.

8, 9, 10. The condition for convection and cloud formation is that the path curve for rising air (see p. 107) should lie to the right of the environment curve. This is likely to be achieved later in the day when the surface dry-bulb temperature increases. Assuming a rise of 5°, a dry adiabat may be drawn (BC) to the right of the environment curve. Convection is thus possible but a theoretical limit is reached at C (1,000 ft.), for here the rising air has cooled to the temperature of its environment and has no impulse to rise further. No cloud formation is yet possible, since the air remains unsaturated.

But with a further 2° increase of surface dry-bulb temperature, a dry adiabat (DE) may be drawn, which reaches the dew-point line at E. In other words, the rising air becomes saturated at E, and with continued ascent, cools at the S.A.L.R., its path being represented by the saturated adiabat EF. E is the condensation level or cloud base (about 1,600 ft.), and the cloud top is at F (3,600 ft.) where the path curve meets the environment curve. A surface temperature of 44° is, therefore, the minimum required to produce convection cloud.

Similarly, a surface dry-bulb temperature of 50° would make cloud possible between 2,600 ft. and about 3,950 ft., the path of rising air being represented by GHJ. If, however, the surface temperature were to reach 60·5°, cloud would have disappeared: it would not be possible to draw, from L, a saturated adiabat lying to the right of the environment curve. A further rise of temperature (to 69·5°) would ' break' the inversion (MN), and cloud would once again be possible, with base at 6,200 ft., and top (Fig. 49) at about 16,000 or 17,000 ft. But day maximum temperatures are not likely to exceed 55° at this time of year.

It will by now be apparent how the possibilities of convection cloud depend on the relation between slopes on the diagram. It must also be realized that no single air layer must be treated in isolation. For ex-example, cloud is possible between 2,500 and 4,600 ft., although this part of the environment curve is stable when considered by itself. Clearly, conditions below 2,500 ft. are also significant, and with a sufficiently high surface temperature, there is enough energy available to overcome the stability above.

11–14. The freezing level (about 8,200 ft. in this example) is important in relation to the Bergeron theory of precipitation. In this case, we have seen that cloud tops are not likely to achieve anything approaching this height. Showers would therefore not be forecast. For thunderstorm development, a minimum convection cloud thickness of 10,000 ft. is generally considered necessary. In order to determine the minimum surface temperatures that would be required to produce either of these conditions, it would be necessary to interpolate, on the diagram, a saturated adiabat, of the requisite length, which lies everywhere to the right of the environment curve. From the point where this adiabat meets the dew-point line, a dry adiabat drawn to the base of the graph would give the required surface temperature. In the example of Fig. 50 $69 \cdot 5°$ would be the lowest temperature to satisfy both conditions.

15. All the above considerations apply to free convectional ascent, resulting from surface heating. Forced ascent (e.g. against high ground) is a different matter, since it ignores completely the stability conditions of the air. The surface air in Fig. 49, if bodily lifted, would rapidly cool to even the 0600 hour dew-point of $36°$, and cloud would result. Forced ascent is particularly important in the case of conditionally unstable air, which is lifted unwillingly, as it were, while it remains dry (and stable), but, once saturated, becomes unstable, encouraging renewed ascent (see example in 'Climatology', Fig. 17).

The example of Fig. 49 is quite typical of anticyclonic conditions in Polar Maritime air, over inland districts, with a cold clear inversion by night giving way to the familiar cumulus sky of late morning and afternoon. The student should never be content to regard these exercises as purely academic, but should always try to relate them to the readily observable weather conditions which they set out to depict. He should plot some recent ascents, from the nearest or most appropriate station, and see how the weather, either from recollection or from the *Daily Weather Report*, agreed with that expected from the atmospheric structure. The plotting can conveniently be done on tracing paper laid over the framework of lines on Fig. 49.

Section II. The Long-term Plan: Climatic Maps and Data

Contrasted Cartographical Methods of Meteorology and Climatology

The foregoing exercises have been concerned with the state of the atmosphere at a moment of time, i.e. with 'Weather'. The exercises that follow will be concerned with the average conditions of the atmosphere over a period of time, i.e. with climate.

It is curious that while the great majority of meteorological charts are 'synoptic', combining on one map a simultaneous presentation of nearly all the important and relevant elements of the weather, climatic charts rarely show more than one element at a time. There are pressure and wind maps, temperature maps, rainfall maps, cloudiness maps, and many more—but no synoptic climatic maps. This strange default is the more surprising because climate, as an important influence in the geographical environment, has been the object of attention by geographers for a very long time. Now geographers take a pride in their ability to integrate the totality of phenomena in a synthesis of the region. Moreover they fully appreciate the synthetic merits of the topographic map, provided by the cartographer, of the geological map, provided by the geologist, and of the weather map, provided by the meteorologist. The elements of climate are no less intimately inter-related than the elements of meteorology or of geology, and much more closely integrated than the diversity of phenomena, physical and cultural, whose distribution is displayed on the topographic sheet. There is no call to take the climatic map to pieces, as has been done in the previous sections; it has never been put together. Here would seem to be a field of experiment and research in cartographical presentation waiting for the attention of the geographically minded climatologist into which the student might adventure on his own initiative.

Sources of Climatic and Hydrographic Data

For each exercise that follows a complete set of data is provided, but the student or teacher may wish to carry out similar analyses for other stations, e.g. in a region which is being specially studied, or he may wish to experiment with other methods of his own invention: for these purposes he will need to know where the data may be found. The Climatological Section of the Meteorological Office, at Headstone Drive, Harrow, will supply, on request, and on payment of a small search fee, any data that are available. The Annual volumes of the *Reseau Mondial* (available 1910–32 inclusive) give full information for every month in each year on temperature, pressure, and precipitation for 1,500 stations (about two for every 10° square of latitude and

114   THE SKIN OF THE EARTH

longitude) over the world. The difference from the normal is given in
each case, so the normal can easily be calculated from this. This is a
large and expensive publication, not easy to come by, but large collec-
tions of figures are ready to hand in *World Weather Records*, published
by the Smithsonian Institute, which gives the mean monthly pressure,
temperature and rainfall for each year, often for fifty years or more, at
about 500 stations. Most text-books of Climatology supply figures of
mean annual temperature and rainfall; Brooks, in his *Climate in Every-
day Life*, includes some data on relative humidity and days of rain.
The U.S. Department of Agriculture Year Book for 1941 (*Climate and
Man*) adds a large volume of statistical information about the U.S.A.,
including dates of killing frosts. But the fullest source of the most varied
information is printed in the various regional volumes of the *Handbuch
der Klimatologie*, whose completion, unfortunately, was prevented by the
World War.

For Britain the *Books of Normals* give data on Temperature (Maximum, Minimum and Mean), Rainfall, Sunshine, Wind Direction and
Force, Humidity, and Visibility. The monthly supplement to the *Daily
Weather Report* provides interesting summaries of the number of occasions (during the month) when particular phenomena have occurred
or particular values have been attained.

Hydrographic data are abundant in the U.S.A. and can be found
in numerous publications such as:

>   *Rainfall and Runoff*. Foster, 1949.
>   *Stream Flow*. Grover and Harrington, 1943.
>   *River Discharge*. Hoyt and Grover, 1930.

Many continental countries have carried out fairly full river surveys
and data may be obtained, at second hand, from Pardé's *Fleuves et
Rivières*, 1933, and from the *Atlas de France*.

Britain has been backward in this activity, but the *Final Report of
the Investigation of Rivers* by the Royal Geographical Society, 1916, contains much information about the Severn, the Exe, and the Medway.
In 1936 the Ministry of Health began the publication of the *Surface
Water Year Book of Great Britain* containing records of all the rivers that
had been gauged at the time. Two volumes appeared, 1935–6 and
1936–7. New legislation has laid an obligation on River Boards to
measure the discharges and levels of waterways under their jurisdiction;
much fuller information should soon be available.

Limitations of Climatic Data

From the very nature of the observational data on which it is based
climatology cannot be an exact science. The limitations of the observational data should be constantly borne in mind and they should not
be pressed into underwriting a claim for accuracy that they cannot

honour. Mean monthly rainfall, for example, is a mathematical fiction; the monthly precipitation in one January may be double that of the next. The longer the records are kept the more constant the mean becomes, but the mean of one 35-year period may differ from the next by 2 per cent. or more. For these reasons mean temperatures can only be relied upon to the nearest degree and rainfall to the nearest inch, and the appearance of precision attained by using a second place of decimals is quite illusory. Wind direction and wind force fluctuate, the former is generally read to 8 points of the compass only and the latter is often based on estimates on the Beaufort Scale with intervals of several miles per hour between 'forces' which are not even regularly spaced. Sunshine is inefficiently recorded by an instrument that begins to record somewhere in the neighbourhood of an arbitrary threshold value. Relative humidity is calculated by a process in which very small errors of reading the wet- and dry-bulb thermometers are magnified in the result.

It would clearly be unwise to treat such crudely measured values as if they were precise quantitative statements, and it is a waste of time to submit to refined mathematical analysis material of such fundamental unreliability.

Furthermore, geographers will hardly need to be reminded that meteorological data, which are physical measurements of certain states of the atmosphere, do not affect animate or inanimate things in a manner proportional to their numerical value. The value of rain depends on other things than simple quantity, the sensation of warmth or cold is inadequately recorded by the thermometer alone. There are meteorological and climatic states that the geographer and the biologist want to assess which are not recorded at all, in fact no means have yet been devised of recording them. In the meanwhile it is necessary to use what the meteorologist provides and to make the most of what we have.

Units of Climatic Data; Conversion

In general English-speaking countries use the Fahrenheit scale of temperature and inches as a measure of precipitation: all other countries use the centigrade[1] scale and metric units. When data are collected from diverse sources it will generally be necessary, in order to state all values in the same units, to convert one to the other. The arithmetical conversion is laborious and if no conversion tables are ready to hand time will be saved if the student will immediately make for himself a line converter.

Ex. The simplest method is to use graph paper, and, for the temperature scale, place 32° F. opposite 0° C. Mark off units of 5 (or 2½)

[1] Note that the centigrade scale is also called 'Celsius', after its inventor, and that the absolute scale is the same as centigrade plus 273° (the 'absolute' zero is − 273° centigrade).

upwards and downwards and number these for the Fahrenheit scale. On the other side of the line mark off units of 9 (or $4\frac{1}{2}$) and number these for the centigrade scale. For inches and millimetres the conversion is not so simple since 1 in. = 2·54 cm. or 25·4 mm. A very approximate conversion can be done by assuming 2 in. = 5 cm., but at 20 in. the error is already 0·8 cm, or about a third of an inch, which is not negligible. The easiest way of making an accurate scale is simply to draw a 10-in. vertical line on graph paper, mark the inches on one side and, from the scale on your ruler, mark the centimetres and millimetres on the other; 25·4 cm. will come opposite the 10-in. mark. Note that 10 on the inches scale can be used for 1, or for 100, or for 1,000. If 10 in. is inconveniently long for carrying about, use half scale.

Alternatively the well-known geometrical construction for the proportional subdivision of a line could be used but it is neither so quick nor so accurate as the above simple method. It could, however, be used for constructing a conversion table for such awkward equivalents as:

Pressure 1,000 mb. = 750·1 mm. = 29·53 in.
Wind speed 1 mile per hour = 0·4470409 metres per second
1 knot = 1·1515 miles per hour
River discharge 1·86 cusecs. = 1 million gallons per day.

Such simple ratios can, however, be more conveniently shown on a home-made 'quograph' from which the answer to any multiplication or division sum can be read off. The method of construction is simple, but the graph needs to be very carefully drawn. The vertical and hori-

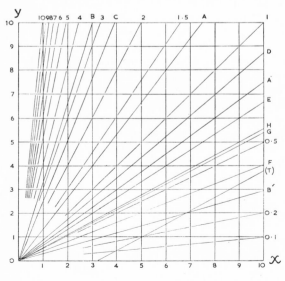

FIG. 50.—Skeleton quograph with some conversion lines

zontal scales of the graph paper represent the divisor and dividend, the diagonal lines represent the quotient (see Fig.50). It may be used for working out such things as yield (bushels per acre) from production and area, speed (miles per hour) from distance and time, precipitation –evaporation ratios, &c.

When large numbers of quotients need to be calculated rapidly it is convenient to draw two Indian ink lines at right angles on a square of tracing paper. This frame of reference can be moved over the graph to coincide with given values of divisor and dividend and the quotient read off at their intersection.

Fig. 50 is a skeleton quograph on which the following conversion ratios have been drawn.

		y			x
A	1,000	mb.	=	750	mm.
A'	750	mm.	=	1,000	mb.
B	1,000	mb.	=	29·5	in. ($\times$ 10)
B'	29·5	in. ($\times$ 10)	=	1,000	mb.
C	750	mm.	=	29·5	in. ($\times$ 10)
D	1	knot	=	1·1515	m.p.h.
E	1	m.p.h.	=	1·47	ft./sec.
F	1	in.	=	2·54	cm.
G	1	million gals./day.	=	1·86	cusecs.
H	5	centigrade degrees	=	9	Fahrenheit degrees
T	$\begin{cases} 5° \\ 0° \end{cases}$	C. C.	= =	32 + 9° 32°	F. F.

All quotient lines and all conversion lines start from zero except T which, of course, starts at 0° C. and 32° F. and must be used strictly in accordance with the scale shown. Divisor and dividend cannot, as in other cases, be multiplied or divided by 10 as convenient.

Conversions made by the quograph are only approximate, the accuracy diminishes in all directions away from the top right-hand corner. The graph is most accurate and most easily read in the neighbourhood of the 45° diagonal, and values of 5, 6, 7, 8, and 9 (on Fig. 50) are too closely crowded to be finely subdivided. To get the best results, however, one of the scales can be varied to make the quotient come in the neighbourhood of the 45° diagonal, e.g. for conversion of millibars to inches the same lengths might be made to represent 1,000 mb. on the vertical scale and, say, 40 in. (an easy value to subdivide) on the horizontal. For still greater accuracy one can construct, on a much larger scale, only that portion in the top right-hand corner that will contain all the answers (i.e. between 950 and 1,050 mb.).

Ex. Given that 1 cu. ft. per second (1 cusec.) = 0·0283 cu. metres per second, construct a graph for the conversion to cubic metres per second of the yearly discharge of a river, which varied between 600 and 1,000 cusecs, during the period under examination.

Wind Direction: Reliability

Wind roses provide a straightforward and satisfactory method of presenting visually the facts about the direction of the wind. Most examples incorporate the device of varying the thickness of the radiating lines to represent winds of different strength. Data for their construction may be found in the *Book of Normals* for the British Isles and in the *Handbuch der Klimatologie* for other regions. They provide a valuable corrective to the often misleading maps of 'prevailing winds', which may prevail by only a small margin over those from some other direction and only rarely prevail over *all* other directions.[1]

Investigate the magnitude of this margin on Fig. 51 which shows the North Atlantic divided into squares of 5° sides (latitude and longitude). The upper figure (in italics) gives the prevailing direction of the wind in degrees clockwise from north. The lower figure (roman type) gives the percentage frequency of occasions on which the wind is above force 2 on the Beaufort scale (i.e. not light or variable) and is within the 90° quadrant of which the prevailing wind is the centre.

Ex. 1. Draw isopleths of percentage frequency at 10 per cent. intervals. Normal percentage (i.e. no prevalence) would be 25; the occurrence of a few figures smaller than this is due to the elimination of calms and light winds from the calculation.

2. Using a protractor, place in each square a wind arrow flying with the prevailing wind. Make the length of the arrow proportional to the percentage frequency of the prevailing wind and thicken all arrows in squares with more than 50 per cent. frequency.

Sunshine: Monthly Incidence

Charts of isonephs and isohels are given in Bartholomew's *Atlas of Meteorology* and well repay examination. Theoretically at any place on earth the sun may shine, because it is above the horizon, for half the year, i.e. for $12 \times 365\frac{1}{4}$ hours per annum (4,383 hours). The sunniest parts of Britain receive about 1,500 hours, rather more than a third of the possible.

The possible hours of sunshine in any one month vary with the latitude of the station and the declination of the particular month and can be obtained from an almanac. For the latitudes of the British Isles

---

[1] The constancy of the Trade Winds has been investigated by P. R. Crowe in the *Transactions* of the Institute of British Geographers, 1949, and is shown in the new *Oxford Atlas*. The winds of the Indian Ocean are examined by E. H. G. Dobby in the *Geog. Rev.*, 1945.

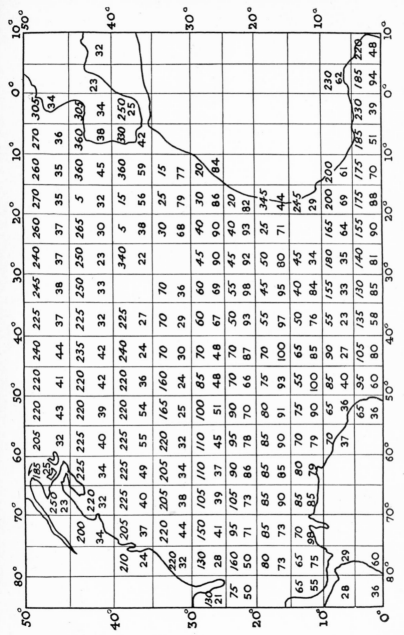

FIG. 51.—Reliability of winds in the North Atlantic (July)

9

the possible duration per month, i.e. sun above the horizon, is as follows.

TABLE 5: *Possible hours of sunshine*

Lat., ° N.	J.	F.	F. Leap Year	M.	A.	M.	J.	Jy.	A.	S.	O.	N.	D.
58	219	257	267	361	426	510	532	530	467	378	312	232	197
56	232	263	273	362	420	499	516	516	459	376	316	239	211
54	243	268	279	363	417	490	503	505	453	375	322	251	225
52	251	273	284	365	412	481	491	494	446	374	324	258	230
50	262	278	289	365	410	473	482	485	442	373	327	266	246

Ex. In the following table the average duration of bright sunshine is given for a number of stations distributed over the British Isles. Complete the table by calculating the proportion of daylight in which the sun shines. This percentage of sunshine can be plotted on an outline map and isopleths drawn to demonstrate the distribution of 'sunniness' for January and July.

TABLE 6: *Mean monthly sunshine hours*

Station	Approx. Lat.	January			July		
		Daylight	Sunshine	% of possible	Daylight	Sunshine	% of possible
Lerwick	60		22			137	
Kirkwall	59		34			135	
Inverness	57½		45			146	
Dundee	56½		53			165	
Oban	56½		33			149	
Dumfries	55		42			163	
Scarborough	54		45			170	
Skegness	53½		56			199	
Cambridge	52		53			192	
Southend	51½		56			210	
Buxton	53		30			164	
Birmingham	52½		44			171	
Oxford	52	251	56	22	494	189	35
Ross on Wye	52		55			192	
Kew	51½		44			194	
Dover	51		60			216	
Bournemouth	51		66			220	
Blackpool	54		46			196	
Manchester	53½		12			139	
Aberystwyth	52		57			179	
Rhayader	52		45			169	
Cardiff	51½		54			211	
Ilfracombe	51		47			206	
Falmouth	50		60			217	

TABLE 7: *Monthly average duration of bright sunshine for each hour of the day at Valencia (Ireland)*

Figures show hundredths of an hour

	a.m. 4	5	6	7	8	9	10	11	12	1	2	3	4	5	6	7	8 p.m.
J.						01	13	24	29	28	24	15	02				
F.					01	11	26	33	35	35	34	34	28	16	02		
M.				01	15	34	41	46	47	47	45	43	39	34	18	02	
A.			01	16	35	42	46	49	48	48	48	47	45	41	37	21	08
M.		15	38	46	48	50	51	53	54	55	55	54	53	50	41	23	01
J.	01	20	34	41	44	47	48	48	49	51	51	50	47	43	37	28	04
Jy.		10	20	26	30	35	38	40	42	42	43	42	40	38	30	18	02
A.		06	21	31	37	39	41	42	42	43	42	40	36	29	19	05	
S.			02	19	34	41	44	45	46	47	46	43	38	22	05		
O.				02	21	34	39	41	41	43	41	36	25	06			
N.					03	28	32	34	35	34	31	21	05				
D.					01	07	21	26	25	24	19	10					

Ex. Draw lines enclosing the 50s, 40s, &c. like the one shown (40). This is a useful method of combining hourly and monthly frequencies; it produces a picture well worth studying and draws attention to such features of the Valencia climate as the sunniness of May and of the middle of the day compared with cloudier mornings and afternoons, the strong tendency to morning cloud in July, &c.

Insufficient attention is, in general, devoted to the diurnal march of phenomena in climatic description. This method can be applied successfully to the study of the diurnal incidence of rain, temperature, wind, &c. (see pp. 136 and 147).

Temperature: Mean Lapse Rate and Latitude

The figures provided in Table 8 may be taken as representative of their latitude. They are derived from a great number of upper air ascents and high flights. Either the summer or the winter figure can be used for the exercise as follows:

Ex. Draw a horizontal line on graph paper to represent the quadrant of the earth from equator to pole and mark degrees of latitude.

For either summer or winter erect perpendiculars at the appropriate latitude for each place and, to any convenient scale, mark temperatures at each height.

TABLE 8: Mean Upper air temperatures (° A.)

Station Latitude and Longitude → Height (km.)	KIRUNA 68° N. 20° E. Summer	KIRUNA Winter	EKATERINBOURG 57° N. 61° E. Summer	EKATERINBOURG Winter	LINDENBERG 52° N. 14° E. Summer	LINDENBERG Winter	PARIS 49° N. 2° E. Summer	PARIS Winter	PAVIA 45° N. 9° E. Summer	PAVIA Winter	ST. LOUIS 39° N. 90° W. Summer	ST. LOUIS Winter	AGRA 27° N. 78° E. Summer	AGRA Winter	BATAVIA 6° S. 107° E. Summer	BATAVIA Winter	VICTORIA NYANZA 1° S. 33° E. Summer	VICTORIA NYANZA Winter	Height (km.)
20									222	219					—	—	—	—	20
19									220	219					—	—	189	—	19
18									219	223					—	—	190	—	18
17									219	219					189	189	197	—	17
16									219	217					194	192	203	—	16
15	—	—	—	—	—	—	226	214	219	216	222	211	—	—	200	197	207	—	15
14	225	214	225	—	224	216	226	215	217	217	217	211	—	—	205	204	211	—	14
13	222	218	225	—	222	216	226	216	216	216	214	214	—	—	213	213	216	—	13
12	222	216	225	—	221	215	225	216	217	214	217	215	233	221	223	222	223	—	12
11	224	214	224	210	221	216	224	217	220	214	225	217	235	227	230	231	231	—	11
10	228	214	223	212	224	218	226	221	224	219	230	221	241	233	239	239	239	—	10
9	235	221	229	216	230	223	232	227	232	224	239	226	248	238	246	247	246	—	9
8	243	226	238	223	237	229	239	235	240	231	247	231	255	244	253	254	251	—	8
7	250	232	245	232	244	237	247	242	247	238	255	240	260	251	260	261	258	—	7
6	257	239	253	239	251	244	254	249	255	245	263	249	267	257	266	266	263	—	6
5	263	244	259	246	258	251	261	256	262	253	270	255	272	264	271	272	269	—	5
4	269	251	264	253	265	258	267	262	268	260	275	261	278	271	277	277	275	—	4
3	273	256	270	259	270	264	272	268	274	266	280	266	284	277	282	283	281	—	3
2	278	259	277	265	275	269	277	273	280	271	284	270	291	283	288	289	288	—	2
1	282	264	284	269	281	273	282	276	286	275	292	272	298	287	294	294	—	—	1
0	284	254	294	265	287	274	284	277	292	277	298	274	302	289	299	299	296	—	0

Draw isopleths, which will be sections of isothermal surfaces.

Put in the tropopause and notice its height and temperature at each latitude.

Insert on the graph, at their appropriate latitude, perpendiculars for the high altitude towns and mountains, given in Table 9. Compare their mean temperature of the appropriate season (given in the table) with that of the free air at their latitude and altitude. Repeat for the other season.

TABLE 9: *Temperature at high-level stations*

	Altitude	Latitude	Temperature (° F.)	
			Jan.	July
Nairobi	5500	1	64	59
Quito	9350	0	55	55
Mexico City	7400	19	54	62
Simla	7230	31	42	65
Jerusalem	2450	32	44	73
Denver	5290	40	30	72
Pikes Peak	14110	39	2	40
Leh	11500	34	17	63
Sonnblick	10097	47	9	34

Yearly Range of Temperature in the U.S.A.

January and July temperatures are provided in Table 10 for 58 stations, fairly evenly distributed, and from these the annual range of temperature can be calculated. The coldest month is always January, but in a very few cases the hottest month is not July (e.g. San Francisco), but if the July temperatures are used the errors will be few in number and of little significance.

Ex. In this exercise, since we are dealing only with temperature differences, there is no need for any reduction to sea level values.

TABLE 10: *January and July temperatures, U.S.A.*

No.	Station	Lat., ° N.	Long., ° W.	Altitude, ft.	Jan., ° F.	July, ° F.	Range
1	Austin	40	117	6594	27	69	
2	Boisé City	44	116	2770	29	73	
3	Colon	9	79	36	80	80	
4	S. Salvador	14	89	2230	66	71	
5	Leon	31	101	5920	39	59	
6	Mazatlan	23	106	13	57	79	
7	Mexico City	19	99	7407	35	47	
8	Monterrey	26	100	1731	40	78	
9	Oaxaca	16	97	5157	48	59	
10	Abilene	32	100	1738	44	82	

No.	Station	Lat., ° N.	Long., ° W.	Altitude, ft.	Jan., ° F.	July, ° F.	Range
11	Albany	43	74	97	29	73	
12	Bismarck	47	101	1674	9	70	
13	Charleston	33	80	25	50	80	
14	Cheyenne	41	105	6088	26	67	
15	Chicago	42	88	823	26	74	
16	Cincinnatti	39	85	628	33	77	
17	Corpus Christi	28	97	20	56	82	
18	Denver	40	105	5291	30	72	
19	Detroit	42	83	730	25	73	
20	Eastport	45	67	76	21	60	
21	El Paso	32	107	3762	45	81	
22	Galveston	29	95	54	54	82	
23	Hatteras	35	76	11	46	78	
24	Hellena	47	112	4110	20	68	
25	Key West	24	82	22	69	84	
26	Little Rock	35	92	357	42	80	
27	Mobile	31	88	57	51	80	
28	Nashville	36	87	546	39	79	
29	New York	41	74	314	31	74	
30	North Platte	41	101	2821	23	74	
31	Omaha	41	96	1105	22	77	
32	Phoenix	32	112	1108	50	90	
33	Portland	46	123	153	39	67	
34	Red Bluff	40	122	332	45	81	
35	St. Louis	39	90	568	32	79	
36	St. Paul	45	93	837	12	72	
37	Salt Lake City	41	112	4360	29	77	
38	San Diego	33	117	87	54	67	
39	San Francisco	38	122	155	49	57	
40	San Luis Obispo	35	121	200	52	64	
41	Santa Fé	35	106	7013	29	68	
42	Spokane	48	117	1929	27	69	
43	Washington	39	77	112	34	76	
44	Merida	21	90	72	65	63	
45	Duluth	47	92	1133	10	66	
46	Eureka	41	124	64	47	55	
47	Harrisburg	40	77	361	29	75	
48	Indianapolis	40	86	822	28	76	
49	Miami	26	80	5	66	82	
50	Montgomery	32	86	240	48	82	
51	Olympia	47	122	—	39	63	
52	Oswego	42	76	335	24	69	
53	Pike's Peak	38	105	14111	2	40	
54	Pine Bluff	34	92	215	43	82	
55	Raleigh	36	78	390	40	73	
56	Salem	45	123	120	41	66	
57	San Antonio	29	98	701	53	83	
58	Yuma	33	115	141	55	91	

(1) Calculate the range by subtraction; (2) plot the figures on an outline map; and (3) interpolate isopleths. Explain their spacing and directions.

Isanomalies of Temperature in the Northern Hemisphere.[1]

This is an application of a valuable method to which we shall frequently have recourse, the 'method of differences'. In 'isothermal' or 'isobaric' maps, such as are reproduced in all atlases, the temperatures or pressures are reduced to sea level in order to make the values comparable by eliminating the factor of altitude. The reduction is done by means of a formula based on the average decrease of pressure or temperature with altitude. On any particular day and in any particular place this formula may not, and in the case of temperature almost certainly will not be true, but as an average it gives the closest available approximation.

Ex. Concentrating first on the January figures, our first step, therefore, is to reduce the temperature for each of the 131 stations to their sea-level equivalents on the assumption that temperature decreases with altitude at 3° F./1,000 ft. These may be entered in the column provided.[2]

At this stage it is well to remember that our isopleths on the finished map will be fairly widely spaced (perhaps at intervals of 5°), so that a high degree of accuracy is not called for; the nearest whole number is good enough.

Having eliminated altitude as a factor we now proceed to eliminate latitude by finding the average sea-level temperature of each latitude and expressing the sea-level temperature of each station as a departure from this mean.

The average temperature along the parallel of latitude could be calculated by taking the mean temperature at places evenly spaced along that parallel (say 36 values at each 10° of longitude). Such a figure would be meaningless and in any case is unattainable since more than half of the 'stations' would be at sea. We will therefore content ourselves with the mean temperature of land stations along the parallel. In fairness these should be evenly spaced; or at least stations occurring widely apart should be 'weighted' to increase their effect and those close together should have their 'weight' reduced by eliminating some.

---

[1] *N.B.* This exercise, and some others, involves a great deal of simple but laborious calculation. If worked in class the labour can be divided, each group taking a certain batch of figures and dictating their results.

[2] It is sometimes a saving of labour to construct a ready-reckoner graph of the type shown on p. 116, by which the sea-level temperatures may be read off by inspection, but in this case the simple arithmetic will probably be the quicker method.

TABLE 11: *Anomalies of temperature in the Northern Hemisphere*

No.	Station	Lat., ° N.	Long.	Alt., ft.	Jan., ° F.	S.L. Temp.	Dep.	July, ° F.	S.L. Temp.	Dep.
1	Abassia (Egypt)	30	31E	100	53			81		
2	Entebbe	0	33E	3842	71			69		
3	Freetown (Sierra Leone)	9	13W	224	81			79		
4	Lagos	7	3E	22	81			78		
5	Aden	13	45E	94	76			88		
6	Colombo	7	80E	24	80			81		
7	Hankow	31	114E	110	39			83		
8	Hong Kong	22	114E	100	60			82		
9	Mukden	42	123E	130	8			76		
10	Zikawei	31	121E	25	37			81		
11	Akyab (India)	20	93E	20	70			81		
12	Bangalore	13	78E	3021	69			74		
13	Bombay	19	73E	37	76			81		
14	Cochin	10	76E	9	81			79		
15	Lahore	32	74E	702	55			91		
16	Nagpur	21	80E	1017	69			82		
17	Simla	31	77E	7232	42			65		
18	Monkay (I. China)	21	102E	30	61			83		
19	Saigon	10	107E	40	79			82		
20	Basra (Iraq)	30	48E	22	52			93		
21	Miyako (Japan)	40	142E	100	30			68		
22	Nagasaki	32	130E	420	43			79		
23	Joshin (Korea)	41	129E	15	19			68		
24	Bushire (Persia)	29	49E	14	57			90		
25	Akmolinsk	51	71E	1000	3			68		
26	Barnaul	53	84E	158	3			67		
27	Blagovyestchensk	50	128E	140	−10			70		
28	Dudinka	69	86E	70	−22			53		
29	Irkutsk	52	104E	1300	−4			62		
30	Krasnovodsk	40	53E	70	36			83		
31	Narynsokoye	41	67E	6046	1			63		
32	Okhotsk	59	143E	25	−11			51		
33	Olekminsk	60	120E	350	−31			66		
34	Surgut	61	73E	130	−9			63		
35	Tobolsk	58	68E	300	−2			64		
36	Verkhoyansk	68	133E	400	−50			50		
37	Yeniseisk	58	92E	300	−6			66		
38	Vienna	48	16E	650	27			68		
39	Greenwich	51	0	12	39			62		
40	Valencia	52	10W	—	45			59		
41	Helsingfors	60	25E	34	21			63		
42	Paris	49	3E	200	37			65		
43	Berlin	53	13E	101	30			66		
44	Frankfurt	50	9E	390	32			66		
45	Athens	38	24E	400	48			81		

No.	Station	Lat., °N.	Long.	Alt., ft.	Jan., °F.	S.L. Temp.	Dep.	July, °F.	S.L. Temp.	Dep.
46	Sassari	41	8E	100	46			75		
47	Gjesvar (Norway)	71	25E	20	25			50		
48	Oslo	60	11E	80	25			63		
49	Lisbon	39	9W	300	50			70		
50	Kiev (Russia)	50	30E	600	20			66		
51	Leningrad	60	30E	10	18			63		
52	Orenburg	51	55E	350	5			72		
53	Perm	58	56E	500	3			65		
54	Tiflis (Russia)	42	45E	1100	32			75		
55	Upsala	60	18E	80	25			63		
56	Jumeau (Alaska)	58	134W	80	27			57		
57	Nome ,,	65	165W	22	1			50		
58	Sitka ,,	57	135W	90	32			55		
59	Valdez ,,	61	146W	27	17			54		
60	Calgary (Canada)	51	114W	3389	12			61		
61	Fort Hope	52	88W	100	−8			62		
62	Kamloops	51	120W	1193	23			60		
63	Moose Factory	51	81W	30	−5			61		
64	Q'Appelle	51	104W	2113	0			64		
65	St. John's	49	53W	125	24			59		
66	Victoria	48	123W	85	39			60		
67	Winnipeg	50	97W	760	−4			66		
68	Leon	21	101W	6000	57			70		
69	Colon	0	79W	36	80			80		
70	Merida	21	80W	70	72			81		
71	Abilene	32	100W	1738	44			82		
72	Boston	42	71W	125	26			70		
73	Charleston	33	80W	25	50			87		
74	Cheyenne	41	105W	6088	26			67		
75	Chicago	42	88W	823	26			74		
76	El Paso	32	107W	3762	45			81		
77	Mobile	30	88W	57	51			80		
78	New York	41	74W	314	31			74		
79	Salt Lake City	41	112W	4360	29			77		
80	Red Bluff	40	122W	332	45			81		
81	Horta (Azores)	38	29W	190	59			72		
82	Bermuda	32	65W	151	63			80		
83	Canaries	28	16W	−4	53			68		
84	Thorshaven (Faroes)	62	7W	78	38			51		
85	Wigtot (Green-land)	61	48W	15	23			50		
86	Jacobshaven	69	51W	38	10			46		
87	Vestmanno (Ice-land)	63	20W	42	34			51		
88	Madeira (Funchal)	33	17W	75	59			70		
89	Christianstad (Virgin Is.)	18	65W	24	77			83		
90	Trinidad	11	62W	72	75			78		

No.	Station	Lat. °N.	Long.	Alt., ft.	Jan., °F.	S.L. Temp.	Dep.	July, °F.	S.L. Temp.	Dep.
91	Honolulu	21	158W	88	71			78		
92	Iloilo (Phillipines)	11	123E	19	79			81		
93	Mogador	32	9W	33	57			68		
94	Alexandria	31	30E	105	56			77		
95	Wadi Halfa	22	31E	421	68			88		
96	Port Sudan	20	37E	18	73			92		
97	Tunis	35	10E	141	50			89		
98	Addis Ababa	9	38E	8005	62			57		
99	Singapore	1	103E	10	78			81		
100	Deerness (Orkneys)	59	3W	166	39			54		
101	Tromso	70	19E	27	27			52		
102	Haparanda	66	25E	33	12			59		
103	Bergen	60	5E	66	34			58		
104	Palermo	39	13E	230	51			76		
105	Constantinople	41	29E	246	41			73		
106	Dawson City	65	146W	200	−24			59		
107	Fort Chipewayen	59	113W	699	−13			62		
108	Nairn	56	62W	13	−7			46		
109	Para	1	48W	33	17			78		
110	Kingston	18	77W	49	76			82		
111	Cumberland Sd.	65	65W	0	−32			40		
112	Unalaska (Aleutian Is.)	54	167W	6	32			57		
113	Barrow Point	71	156W	5	−20			41		
114	Green Harbour (Spitzbergen)	77	15E	4	0			40		
115	Libreville	0	10E	101	80			75		
116	New Siberian Islands	75	152E	0	−33			40		
117	McClintock Channel	72	104W	0	−30			40		
118	Parry Island	75	93W	0	−55			36		
119	Fort Norman	65	125W	980	−22			60		
120	Popigaisk	73	111E	50	−31			42		
121	Franz Josef Land	80	58E	0	−20			54		
122	Yamsk	60	155E	16	5			50		
123	Balagan	79	166E	500	−30			44		
124	East Cape	67	170W	0	0			42		
125	Galapagos Islands	0	90W	0	75			73		
126	Fanning Islands	0	175E	0	79			78		
127	Radock Islands	10	170E	0	79			77		
128	Pagan (Ladrone Islands)	7	145W	0	79			76		
129	Laccadive Islands	12	73E	0	77			79		
130	Maldive Islands	4	72E	0	81			79		
131	Halmahera (Moluccas)	0	128E	0	80			80		

In practice we can only deal with 5° zones of latitude and a convenient procedure, admittedly rough, is as follows:

1. Collect all stations between o and 4° N., 5° and 9°, &c. and arrange each group by longitude thus (40°–44° group).

					Long. Diff.	
Sassari	.	.	.	.	41° N.	8° E.	
						12	
Constantinople.		.	.	41	20		
						25	interpolate one
Tiflis	.	.	.	.	42	45	
						8	
Krasnovodsk	.		.	40	53		
						14	
Narynsokoye	.		.	41	67		
						56	interpolate four
Mukden .	.	.	.	42	123		
						6	
Joshin	.	.	.	.	41	129	
						13	
Miyako .	.	.	.	40	142		
Boston	.	.	.	.	42	71° W.	
						3	combine as one
New York	.		.	41	74		
						14	
Chicago .	.	.	.	42	88		
						17	
Cheyenne	.		.	41	105		
						7	
Salt Lake City .		.	.	41	112		
						10	
Red Bluff	.	.	.	40	122		
			average	41			

It appears that, with some notable exceptions, the stations lie about 10° or 12° of longitude apart.

2. Now combine those that are fairly close together, e.g. Boston and New York as one value (the mean of the two) and

3. Interpolate hypothetical stations where those given are too widely separated, e.g. the gap between Narynsokoye and Mukden is 58°. In fairness we should interpolate stations at about 80°, 90°, 100°, and 110° E. The January sea-level temperature at Narynsokoye is − 17°, that at Mukden is 8°. We may therefore put in stations 'W, X, Y, and Z' with − 12, − 7, − 2, and + 3 respectively.

4. The average temperature is now calculated for all stations, original, combined, and interpolated. This is the average temperature for the average latitude of this group of stations, which happens to be 41°.

The reader may feel that this laborious 'weighting' is unnecessary; probably it is, and quite good results will be obtained simply by averaging out the temperatures of the listed stations in each 5° latitude belt.

Whether he does so or not the next step is to plot this temperature on a graph as abscissae with latitude as ordinates. The points so obtained are now joined by a smooth curve and from this graph the average temperature of any latitude in the northern hemisphere can be read off. The sea-level temperature of each station can now be entered in the appropriate column as a departure, positive or negative, from the mean of its latitude. These 'anomalies' are now plotted on a blank outline map of suitable scale and projection and 'isanomalous lines' interpolated in the usual way.

The finished map, from which the effects of altitude and latitude have been eliminated, shows the influence of the remaining climatic factors, especially continentality and oceanic circulation, and from it many useful lessons can be learned.

A July map can also be prepared in the same way.

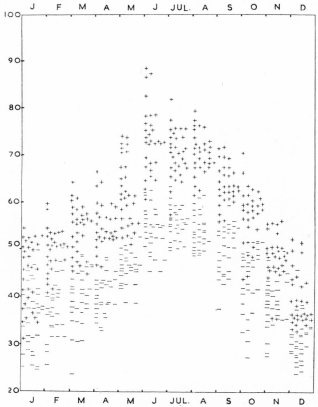

FIG. 52.—Temperature dispersion graph. Daily maximum (+) and minimum (−) at Reading University, 1950

Variation of Daily Maximum and Minimum Temperature

Fig. 52 is a dispersion graph and shows the 365 actual maximum and minimum temperatures recorded at Reading University during one year of observation (1950). Data for repeating the exercise may be obtained from an observers' record book or from a year's set of *Daily Weather Reports.*

Variation of Mean Monthly Temperature

A similar method will serve to show the year-to-year variation of

TABLE 12: *Greenwich. Monthly mean temperature, 1886–1920*

Date	Jan.	Feb.	Mar.	Apr.	May	Jun.	Jul.	Aug.	Sep.	Oct.	Nov.	Dec.	Year
1886	36·3	33·7	39·8	46·6	53·3	57·7	63·1	62·3	59·1	53·3	44·4	36·6	48·85
87	35·8	38·9	37·9	44·2	50·1	61·0	66·5	62·5	54·4	45·2	40·8	38·0	47·94
88	37·9	35·3	38·3	43·5	53·0	58·3	58·0	59·2	55·9	46·0	47·2	40·8	47·78
89	37·2	37·3	40·6	45·7	56·2	61·3	61·0	60·1	55·9	48·7	44·3	37·6	48·82
90	43·6	37·4	43·3	45·6	54·8	58·2	59·6	59·4	59·5	49·6	43·7	29·9	48·72
1891	34·1	38·6	40·2	44·2	50·4	60·2	60·1	58·8	58·9	51·0	43·3	41·1	48·41
92	36·6	39·0	37·3	46·6	54·9	58·1	59·5	61·7	56·4	45·5	45·1	36·6	48·11
93	35·5	41·3	46·0	51·0	57·4	61·6	62·9	65·4	57·1	51·5	42·0	40·7	51·03
94	38·5	41·8	44·5	51·1	50·3	58·6	61·9	59·8	54·3	50·4	46·9	42·4	50·04
95	33·7	29·1	42·8	47·9	55·9	61·3	62·7	62·1	61·9	46·8	47·4	40·3	49·32
1896	40·5	40·4	46·0	49·0	54·7	63·3	65·2	59·4	56·9	46·6	40·5	40·2	50·23
97	35·4	43·2	45·2	46·3	52·4	61·3	64·5	62·9	55·6	51·0	45·8	41·4	50·42
98	43·7	41·3	40·0	48·1	52·0	57·8	61·9	64·8	62·0	53·9	46·1	45·8	51·45
99	42·8	41·9	41·0	47·2	51·1	60·5	65·8	65·5	58·2	49·2	48·0	37·1	50·69
1900	40·4	38·5	39·0	47·8	51·8	59·4	66·6	60·8	58·0	51·3	46·4	45·7	50·47
1901	38·8	36·0	39·3	48·5	53·1	58·6	64·8	62·5	58·0	50·5	41·4	40·0	49·29
02	42·0	35·4	44·6	47·2	48·7	57·6	60·9	59·7	56·2	50·1	44·9	41·5	49·07
03	41·1	45·2	46·2	44·5	53·4	56·1	61·6	59·6	57·5	52·8	45·1	38·7	50·15
04	39·5	39·5	40·5	49·3	53·4	57·7	65·5	61·7	55·4	51·1	42·4	41·1	49·76
05	38·4	42·4	45·1	46·4	53·2	59·5	66·0	60·4	56·2	45·8	41·9	40·6	49·66
1906	42·4	38·7	41·8	45·9	52·9	58·1	63·4	64·7	59·2	54·3	46·5	37·7	50·50
07	38·8	37·8	44·3	46·5	52·6	56·5	58·6	60·5	57·9	51·4	45·3	42·0	49·40
08	36·6	41·8	40·5	55·9	55·9	59·6	62·3	59·7	56·5	53·9	46·7	39·9	49·80
09	38·8	36·9	39·3	49·1	53·1	53·9	60·0	61·8	54·9	52·9	41·9	40·4	48·60
10	40·0	42·0	42·9	46·4	53·0	60·2	58·1	60·8	56·2	53·4	38·9	44·6	49·70
1911	38·2	41·2	41·9	46·3	56·1	59·6	67·3	67·5	60·3	50·5	44·2	44·5	51·50
12	40·2	43·3	45·8	48·5	55·7	58·2	63·3	56·9	53·1	47·4	43·8	45·9	50·20
13	41·1	40·9	44·5	46·8	54·8	58·9	58·5	60·0	57·7	52·7	48·3	41·9	50·50
14	38·4	44·4	43·8	49·8	53·0	59·1	62·5	62·5	57·2	51·6	45·4	42·4	50·80
15	39·7	40·5	41·5	46·5	53·2	58·6	60·6	60·9	57·1	49·0	39·2	44·2	49·30
1916	45·9	39·5	39·1	47·8	55·3	53·6	59·8	62·7	55·8	52·6	44·1	37·2	49·50
17	35·5	35·1	38·1	42·1	56·5	62·3	62·2	60·6	58·7	46·9	46·8	35·9	48·40
18	39·6	43·5	42·9	44·1	55·6	57·2	61·3	62·2	55·7	49·7	43·3	46·1	50·10
19	37·8	35·7	40·1	45·4	56·4	59·6	57·5	63·6	57·3	45·3	39·0	43·0	48·40
20	42·4	43·4	46·4	48·2	55·5	59·7	59·4	57·8	57·0	51·3	43·5	40·7	50·40
M'ns.	38·8	39·7	41·9	47·0	53·3	59·2	62·6	61·6	57·2	50·0	43·6	40·3	49·60

TABLE 13: *Maximum, Minimum,*

Colombo (24'), 6° 54" N. 79° 55' E.

	Mean				Extreme		
Monthly	Max.	Min.	Diurnal range		Max.	Min.	Range
J.	80	87	72		102	62	
F.	81	88	73		99	62	
M.	82	90	74		102	63	
A.	83	90	76		102	67	
M.	83	88	77		104	65	
J.	82	87	77		99	65	
Jy.	81	86	77		100	65	
A.	81	86	77		99	66	
S.	81	86	76		99	63	
O.	80	86	75		100	65	
N.	80	87	74		112	64	
D.	80	87	73		110	64	

Mean annual temperature
Mean annual range
Annual extreme range

Scilly Isles, 49° 58' N. 6° 18' W.

	Mean				Extreme		
Monthly	Max.	Min.	Diurnal range		Max.	Min.	Range
J.	46	49	42		57	25	
F.	66	49	42		57	27	
M.	46	50	43		59	30	
A.	49	53	45		66	32	
M.	53	57	49		67	38	
J.	58	62	54		75	41	
Jy.	61	65	57		75	48	
A.	61	65	57		75	50	
S.	59	63	55		73	44	
O.	54	57	50		69	38	
N.	50	53	47		61	29	
D.	47	51	44		58	30	

Mean annual temperature
Mean annual range
Annual extreme range

and Mean Temperatures

Calcutta (21′), 22° 32′ N. 88° 24′ E.

	Mean				Extreme		
	Monthly	Max.	Min.	Diurnal range	Max.	Min.	Range
J.	67	83	49		88	44	
F.	71	90	51		98	46	
M.	80	98	60		103	50	
A.	86	103	68		107	61	
M.	86	101	70		107	65	
J.	85	98	73		108	70	
Jy.	84	93	75		98	68	
A.	83	92	75		94	74	
S.	83	92	75		95	72	
O.	81	91	68		94	63	
N.	73	87	58		91	51	
D.	87	81	50		85	45	

Mean annual temperature
Mean annual range
Annual extreme range

Cambridge (41′), 52° 13′ N. 0° 6′ E.

	Mean				Extreme		
	Monthly	Max.	Min.	Diurnal range	Max.	Min.	Range
J.	37	44	31		51	23	
F.	38	47	32		53	20	
M.	42	51	33		60	28	
A.	46	57	35		68	32	
M.	52	63	41		69	39	
J.	58	70	49		74	45	
Jy.	62	73	52		80	50	
A.	61	72	51		78	49	
S.	57	67	47		73	44	
O.	49	59	42		64	36	
N.	44	50	35		53	31	
D.	38	45	33		49	24	

Mean annual temperature
Mean annual range
Annual extreme range

the mean, the maximum, or the minimum for each month. Data of monthly means may be obtained from *World Weather Records* which supplied Table 12 (p. 131).

Ex. In twelve (monthly) and one (annual) columns place a dot at the appropriate temperature for each of the 420 monthly and 35 annual means. The dots should be placed up the middle of the column except when nearly identical temperatures occur twice or more times, when they can be placed side by side. A generous piece of graph paper will be required for clarity of effect.

Dispersion graphs will be referred to again in connexion with rainfall, for which they are more often used. Methods of examining the degree of the dispersion will be treated there (pp. 152–5).

Ranges of Temperature

Ex. 1. From the data supplied in Table 13, calculate:

a. Mean diurnal range for each month (mean max. — mean min.).

b. Mean extreme range for each month (extreme max. — extreme min.)

c. Mean annual range (mean of hottest month — mean of coldest month.)

d. Annual extreme range (mean max. of hottest month — mean min. of coldest month).

From Fig. 52 for Reading, calculate :

e. Absolute monthly range for each month (highest max. temp. recorded in the month — lowest minimum temperature recorded).

f. The absolute extreme range is the highest temperature on record — lowest temperature on record.

Ex. 2. Plot the figures for Colombo, Calcutta, Scilly Isles, and Cambridge as five line-graphs, one above the other, for each of the four stations.

This is the usual method of displaying graphically the annual march of temperature, but some interesting facts such as the comparison between spring and autumn may be revealed if the rise (full line) and fall (broken line) are made to slope in the same sense, as in Fig. 53, i.e. the falling half of the curve is the mirror-image of that in the usual form of temperatue curve.

Ex. Plot the following and compare the rise and fall.

	J.	F.	M.	A.	M.	J.	Jy.	A.	S.	O.	N.	D.
Valencia	44	44	45	48	52	57	59	59	57	52	48	46
Bukarest	26	31	41	52	62	69	73	72	64	53	40	31
Kashgar	22	34	47	61	70	77	80	76	69	56	40	26
San Francisco . . .	49	51	53	54	56	57	57	58	60	59	56	51
Bombay	76	76	80	83	86	84	81	81	81	82	81	77

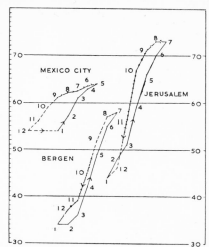

FIG. 53.—Annual rise and fall of temperature compared

Diurnal and Monthly Variation of Temperarure

Ex. The data for Fort William and Ben Nevis are presented in a form similar to that used for sunshine at Valencia (p. 121). In this case, too, lines may be drawn (say at 2° intervals), separating similar temperatures, thus producing a cartogram by which interesting facts will be shown about—

1. the duration of continuous frost on Ben Nevis;
2. the relative importance of diurnal (sun) and seasonal (air mass) factors in the climates;
3. the magnitude of the sun's effect at different seasons at Fort William (cf. sunshine at Valencia, in a similar sort of climate);
4. The hours of attainment of maximum and minimum temperatures.

The Zero of Growth

Ex. In Table 16 the figures for Quito are given in degrees centigrade, those for Wrangell I. and Oxford in degrees Fahrenheit. If the two scales are set up one on either side of the graph paper this will serve as a ready-reckoner for converting one scale to the other (see p. 116). Plot the values for the three stations side by side in zigzag form, joining Jan. min. (night) to Jan. max. (day) to Feb. min. to Feb. max., &c., and note the importance of the nocturnal minimum of temperature.

The value of 43° F. is stated to be the minimum figure for active plant growth. Draw a line at this value and consider the implication

10

TABLE 15: *Mean hourly temperature* (° *C.*)

Fort William

	Midnight	2 a.m.	4	6	8	10	12 noon	2 p.m.	4	6	8	10
Jan.	3·6	3·5	3·5	3·4	3·4	3·5	3·9	4·4	4·1	3·8	3·7	3·6
Feb.	3·3	3·1	3·0	2·9	2·9	3·4	4·4	5·2	5·1	4·3	3·8	3·5
Mar.	4·0	3·6	3·3	3·1	3·4	4·7	5·8	6·5	6·5	5·7	4·8	4·2
Apr.	5·8	5·3	4·9	4·8	5·9	7·8	9·0	9·7	9·8	9·1	7·5	5·4
May	7·9	7·2	6·8	7·2	9·0	10·6	11·8	12·6	12·6	12·0	10·3	8·8
June	11·1	10·4	10·0	10·8	12·4	13·8	14·9	15·7	15·9	15·5	13·7	12·1
July	12·4	11·9	11·6	12·0	13·3	14·6	15·5	16·2	16·3	15·8	14·3	13·1
Aug.	12·3	11·9	11·6	11·6	12·8	14·2	15·1	15·6	15·9	15·2	13·7	12·9
Sept.	10·8	10·4	10·1	10·0	10·8	12·2	13·3	13·9	14·1	13·0	11·8	11·2
Oct.	7·4	7·2	7·0	6·9	7·1	8·1	9·4	9·9	9·7	8·6	8·0	7·7
Nov.	6·3	6·2	6·2	6·1	6·1	6·5	7·3	7·6	7·3	6·8	6·6	6·4
Dec.	4·4	4·3	4·3	4·2	4·3	4·4	4·9	5·1	4·9	4·6	4·5	4·4

Ben Nevis

	Midnight	2 a.m.	4	6	8	10	12 noon	2 p.m.	4	6	8	10
Jan.	− 4·8	− 4·9	− 4·8	− 4·9	− 4·9	− 4·7	− 4·5	− 4·6	− 4·8	− 4·8	− 4·8	− 4·8
Feb.	− 4·5	− 4·6	− 4·6	− 4·7	− 4·8	− 4·4	− 4·0	− 3·9	− 4·0	− 4·4	− 4·4	− 4·4
Mar.	− 4·5	− 4·7	− 4·8	− 4·9	− 4·6	− 4·0	− 3·6	− 3·5	− 3·6	− 4·2	− 4·3	− 4·4
Apr.	− 2·5	− 2·6	− 2·8	− 2·7	− 2·3	− 1·6	− 1·2	− 1·0	− 1·1	− 1·7	− 2·2	− 2·4
May	0	0·2	0·4	0·2	0·4	1·1	1·6	2·0	1·8	1·3	0·6	0·2
June	3·8	3·5	3·3	3·6	4·1	4·7	5·4	5·8	5·8	5·2	4·6	4·0
July	4·8	4·5	4·3	4·4	4·8	5·5	6·1	6·5	6·5	6·1	5·5	5·0
Aug.	4·4	4·2	4·1	4·0	4·4	5·0	5·6	5·9	5·8	5·4	4·9	4·6
Sept.	3·0	2·9	2·7	2·7	3·0	3·5	3·9	4·2	4·0	3·5	3·3	3·1
Oct.	0	0	0·1	0·2	− 0·1	0·4	0·7	0·8	0·6	0·3	0·2	0·1
Nov.	− 1·6	− 1·6	− 1·5	− 1·6	− 1·6	− 1·3	− 1·1	− 1·1	− 1·4	− 1·5	− 1·5	− 1·5
Dec.	− 3·5	− 3·5	− 3·6	− 3·6	− 3·6	− 3·5	− 3·2	− 3·3	− 3·4	− 3·4	− 3·5	− 3·5

for plant life. This point will be referred to below in connexion with accumulated temperature.

TABLE 16: *Mean daily range of temperature*

	Quito, 0° 15′ S., 2,816 m.			Wrangell I., 70° 58′ N., 10 ft.			Oxford, 51° 46′ N., 208 ft.			
	Max., ° C.	Min., ° C.	Mean	Max., ° F.	Min., ° F.	Mean	Max., ° F.	Min., ° F.	Mean	Ac. T.
J.	19·7	8·1	12·9	− 3	− 18	− 11	45·0	35·1	40·1	1
F.	20·0	8·2	12·8	− 7	− 21	− 13	48·8	34·5	40·1	1
M.	19·4	8·5	12·7	− 2	− 18	− 10	49·9	35·7	42·8	2
A.	19·8	8·3	12·8	7	− 6	1	54·8	38·9	46·9	5
M.	19·9	8·2	12·9	22	11	17	62·8	45·0	53·9	11
J.	20·3	7·3	12·9	37	28	33	67·2	49·5	58·3	16
Jy.	21·0	6·8	12·8	42	32	37	70·5	53·3	61·9	20
A.	21·5	6·6	13·0	40	31	35	69·7	53·0	61·3	19
S.	21·6	7·2	13·1	32	25	29	65·1	48·7	56·9	14
O.	20·7	7·6	12·7	21	12	18	57·5	43·6	50·5	8
N.	20·4	7·6	12·7	7	− 5	4	49·1	37·7	43·4	2
D.	20·5	7·8	12·8	1	− 12	− 5	49·5	36·1	40·8	1
Year	20·5	7·7	12·8	17	5	11	56·9	42·6	49·7	100

Accumulated Temperature (Remainder Index)

This is a device for assessing the accumulated warmth, over a period of time, above some threshold value. It can be used either for estimating the warmth available to a plant, using the zero of 43° F. (the Meteorological Office uses 42°) referred to above, or by heating engineers for giving a measure of the deficiency of heat below the threshold of physical comfort (say 65°) to be made good by central heating.

It is clear from the graph just drawn that at Quito growing temperatures are available every day, though growth is probably checked every night. At Oxford growth may occur by day in any month, but does not last through the night until May, and by November the nights are again too cold. At Wrangell I. 43° is never attained, as a mean value, even in the warmest month.

The principal use of 'day-degrees' is in studies by agronomists and plant physiologists in their search for a relationship between growth and temperature in individual plants or crops during the *actual* season of their growth. Calculations are therefore based on the daily maximum and minimum temperatures over that period or even on the continuous record of a thermograph. In climatic study, however, the *mean* availability of accumulated temperature over the year, or a season, is more often useful. This element of the climate shows a fairly high correlation with the distribution of crops and of natural vegetation, at least in temperate climates [1] (see p. 139).

Ex. We may now try estimating accumulated temperature in various ways. The usual unit used is the 'day-degree', i.e. 1° of temperature for one whole day (and night). If 43° is the zero then a day whose mean temperature was 50° has accumulated 7 (50 − 43) day-degrees. With the figures for Quito and Oxford given here it will be easier to calculate 'month-degrees' which can be converted to day-degrees, if desired, by multiplying by the number of days in the month.

Method 1. From the graph you have drawn count up the number of squares (or rectangles according to scale used), with sides 1° high and 1 month long above the zero line (43°).

Method 2. Subtract 43 from the mean temperature of each month and add up the 12 monthly differences.

Method 3. Subtract 43 from the mean annual temperature and multiply by 12.

Method 4. The use of the Air Ministry formula (A.M. form 3300) would be slightly improper since the data in this case are not daily maxima and minima, but mean monthly values. But if it were applied (with a threshold of 43°) it would give, for Oxford, the values set down in the last column. It will be noticed that they are a fraction higher than those obtained by subtracting 43 from the mean in those months when the mean is above 43°. Furthermore some temperature accumulates by virtue of the mid-day maximum even in those months when the mean lies below 43°. At Quito, where the temperature is always above 43° F., the 'official' value would be only slightly higher than that obtained from the mean. Wrangell I., where the temperature never exceeds 43°, is off the bottom of the tables supplied in the Air Ministry form. It accumulates a deficiency of nearly 380 month-degrees, or more than 10,000 day-degrees.

Compare the results achieved by the various methods, calculate the percentage errors and, by examining the monthly totals, note where the errors occur.

Comparison of Limits

When the distribution of two things coincides it does not necessarily follow that they are causally related;[2] but they may be. On the other hand if they do not coincide a direct causal relationship is disproved.

---

[1] A. Austin Miller, *Trans. Inst. Brit. Geog.*, 1952.
[2] The classical exposure of this fallacy is: most people die in bed, therefore bed is a dangerous place.

The method of comparing distributions is much used in Geography as a first step to establishing causal connexions, and the closer the coincidence the more probable is the conclusion.

Ex. The isotherm of 50° F. (10° C.) for the warmest month has long been accepted as marking the limit of tree growth. From the data provided for 143 stations (Table 17) plot this isotherm on a piece of tracing paper laid over the map (Fig. 54) and compare it with the limit of trees shown by the pecked line and stipple Then plot the accumulated temperatures provided in month-degrees for these stations, draw isopleths and consider whether any relationship can be considered to exist.

TABLE 17: *Accumulated temperature, Canada and Alaska*

No.	Station	Warmest month, ° C.	Acc. temp. (° C. above 6° C.), month-degrees
1	St. Johns	15·5	31
2	Port aux Basques	14·5	25
3	Belle Isle	10·4	9
4	Sable Islands	17·2	41
5	Sydney	17·7	43
6	Charlottetown	18·5	47
7	Halifax	18·2	48
9	Harrington Harbour	12·3	17
10	St. John	16·3	40
11	Fredericton	18·9	47
12	Chatham	19·1	47
13	Anticosti Islands	13·8	23
14	Clark City	15·7	28
15	Father Point	14·3	26
16	Chicoutimi	18·2	41
25	Mistasini Post	15·8	27
42	Moose Factory	16·2	30
83	Stewart	14·7	33
85	Telegraph Creek		
86	Atlin	12·2	15
87	Dawson	15·2	25
89	McPherson	14·9	21
90	Good Hope	15·3	21
91	Norman	15·1	22
92	Coppermine	12·2	9
93	Simpson	16·4	28
94	Hay River	15·3	23
95	Smith	15·5	24
96	Fort Vermilion	15·6	28
97	Chipewyan	15·2	23
98	McMurray	16·7	35
99	Port Nelson	12·8	15
99a	Churchill	12·4	12
100	Fort George	12·4	17
101	Great Whale	12·4	9
102	Harrison	8·4	5
103	Chesterfield	9·1	6
104	Nottingham Islands	6·2	0

No.	Station	Warmest month, ° C.	Acc. temp. (° C. above 6° C.), month-degrees
105	Hope's Advance	5·3	0
105a	Chimo	12·3	14
106	Rama	8·2	4
107	Hebron	8·4	5
108	Okak	8·7	5
109	Nain	9·1	6
110	Zoar	10·9	10
111	Hoffenthal	10·4	9
112	Resolution	5·1	0
113	Lake Harbour	7·6	2
114	Pangnirtung	8·3	3
115	Calder	12·9	24
116	Cordova	12·7	22
117	Dutch Harbour	10·9	15
118	Fortmann Hatchery	14·7	33
119	Juneau	14·0	28
120	Kodiak	12·4	21
121	Latouche	12·9	24
122	Sitka	12·6	24
123	Skagway	14·7	30
124	Valdez	12·1	19
125	Wrangell	14·4	33
126	Yakutat	11·8	19
127	Anchorage	13·8	24
128	Kennecott	11·2	14
129	Matanuska	14·3	25
130	Akulurak	10·9	12
131	Dillingham	13·2	22
132	Holy Cross	13·6	20
133	Nome	10·1	10
134	St. Michael	12·1	14
135	St. Paul Islands	8·3	5
136	Barrow	4·5	0
137	Candle	11·5	13
138	Allakaket	14·3	21
139	Eagle	15·1	24
140	Fairbanks	15·7	28
141	Fort Yukon	15·9	26
142	Rampart	15·6	26
143	Tanana	14·8	24

Critical Values: 'Killing Frosts', 'Mean' and 'Standard deviation'

The temperature of 42° or 43° (6° C.) is claimed to be a critical value for plant growth; 'killing frost' is more obviously critical for some plants—those that are killed. But the definition of a killing frost is not easy in terms of temperature; it is not simply marked by freezing point either on the ground or in the screen. It is easier, though not very helpful, to define by the observed results, and in the Atlas of American Agriculture a killing frost is defined as 'a frost, or temperature condition, of sufficient severity to be generally destructive to the staple products of the locality'.

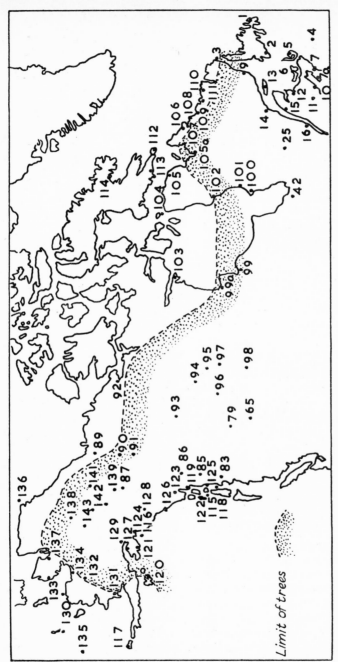

Limit of trees

FIG. 54.—Climatic stations and the limit of trees in sub-arctic North America

By such standards the dates of the last killing frost of spring at Vancouver and Bismark are said to have been as follows:

TABLE 18: *Dates of last killing frost*

	Vancouver, B.C.				Bismark, N.D.			
Year	Date	Year day	Deviation + or −	D^2	Date	Year day	Deviation + or −	D^2
1901	Apr. 24				Jun. 7			
1902	,, 12				Apr. 29			
1903	,, 15				May 5			
1904	,, 23				,, 14			
1905	Mar. 31				,, 12			
1906	Apr. 12				,, 27			
1907	,, 19				,, 14			
1908	,, 28				,, 2			
1909	,, 21				,, 13			
1910	,, 14				,, 17			
Sum								
Mean								

Standard deviation, $\sqrt{\dfrac{\Sigma D^2}{n}}$ =

These data can be used in the first place for an exercise in determining the average variability of the date of its occurrence.

Ex. First convert the date into the 'year day', i.e. February 1st is the 32nd day, March 1st is the 60th day except in leap year (1904 and 1908) when it is the 61st, and so on. Add these together and determine the mean date. Then complete the 'Deviation' column, entering the departures, positive and negative, from this date.

Add these up, ignoring the sign, and find the 'mean deviation'.

To determine the 'standard deviation' square each deviation (D^2), add them together and find the mean $\left(\dfrac{\Sigma D^2}{n}\right)$. The square root of this is the standard deviation.

Frost-free Period and other 'Durations'

It is the practice in the U.S.A. to refer to the period between the last killing frost of spring and the first of autumn as the 'growing season'. This is an unfortunate and misleading use of the term. In England frosts may occur until late in May, by which time the 'growing season' is well advanced, and they may recur in September while things are still growing. Over here a more usual meaning attached to the

TABLE 19: *Duration of growing season*

Station	Average date of first and last killing frost		Duration of growing season	Mean temperature of months above and below 6° C.				Date of crossing threshold		Duration. Days above threshold
	Spring	Fall		Spring		Fall		Spring	Fall	
1	2	3	4	5	6	7	8	9	10	11
Boston	Apr. 13	Oct. 29	199	Apr. 3·5	May 8·3	Oct. 8·5	Nov. 2·7	May 1	Oct. 29	182
Atlantic City	Apr. 6	Nov. 7	215	Mar. 3·5	Apr. 8·5	Nov. 7·4	Dec. 2·3	Apr. 10	Nov. 5	207
Syracuse	Apr. 23	Oct. 22	182	Mar. — 0·8	Apr. 7·1	Oct. 10·9	Nov. 3·7			
Cincinnati	Apr. 12	Oct. 25		Mar. 4·9	Apr. 11·6	Oct. 13·3	Nov. 5·8			
Detroit	Apr. 24	Oct. 18		Mar. 0·7	Apr. 7·8	Oct. 11·3	Nov. 4·1			
Duluth	May 10	Oct. 5		Apr. 2·7	May 8·5	Oct. 6·6	Nov. 1·1			
Omaha	Apr. 14	Oct. 20		Mar. 1·2	Apr. 12·1	Oct. 12·4	Nov. —			
Denver	Apr. 26	Oct. 14		Mar. 3·8	Apr. 8·4	Oct. 10·4	Nov. 5·5			
Spokane	Apr. 12	Oct. 13		Mar. 3·9	Apr. 8·8	Oct. 8·6	Nov. 4·0			
Seattle	Mar. 14	Nov. 24		Feb. 4·8	Mar. 6·8	Nov. 7·3	Nov. 3·4			
Fresno (Cal.)	Feb. 9	Dec. 1		Jan. 7·7		Dec. 7·7	Dec. 5·2			
Yuma	Jan. 12	Dec. 26		Jan. 12·2		Dec. 12·6				

'growing season' would be the period over which the curve of mean temperature is above 42° (the official threshold for the calculation of day-degrees).

In America the threshold temperature for 'life zones' or the 'growing season', when defined by this criterion, is usually 43° F. (6° C.). We may use the figures in Table 19 for a comparison of the 'growing season' as defined (1) in this way (data from the *Handbuch der Klimatologie*, Vol. 2, Amerika), and (2) as defined by the dates of last and first killing frost (data from *Climate and Man*).

Ex. Column 4 can be calculated and completed, but for columns 8, 9 and 10 it is necessary to estimate the date (from columns 5 and 6) on which the temperature curve passes the threshold (6° C.) in spring and again in the fall (from columns 7 and 8). Assuming a steady rise of temperature in spring and a steady fall in autumn this can most easily be done by means of the graph (Fig. 55). The mean temperature of the last month below the threshold in spring is joined to that of the first month above it; where this line cuts the threshold temperature the date is read off. The opposite procedure is followed for the 'fall', the lines sloping down from left to right. Provision is made on this graph for the unequal length of months.

The comparison of columns 4 and 9, when completed, will reveal discrepancies, and will emphasize the necessity for defining, in each study, the sense in which the term 'duration of growing season' is being used. Compare the discrepancies shown at marine and continental stations.

Maps showing the average duration of the season above, or below, a given threshold can be revealing, but they cannot, of course, be very precise. Such duration maps should not pretend to great precision and the unit is better stated in weeks than in days. Satisfied with a degree of approximation of this order it is possible to write down the figures by inspection of the tables of mean monthly figures.

Ex. Using the *Book of Normals* (M.O. 407) of average temperatures for the British Isles.
1. Calculate for as many stations as necessary the duration of mean temperature above 42° F.
2. Plot the values on an outline map and draw isopleths of what might be called the duration of the growing season in the British sense.

Ex. For a map of the duration of the growing season in the American sense (frost-free period) more than enough data are available in *Climate and Man* (about a hundred stations for each state in the Union).

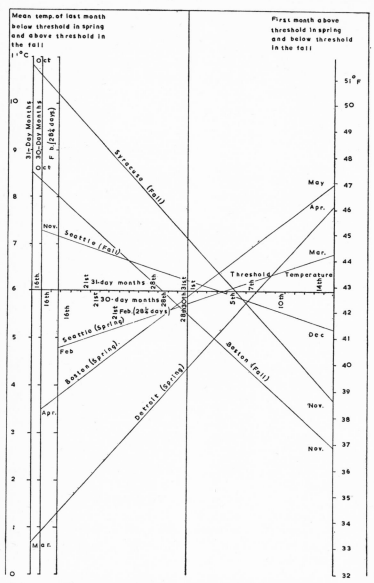

FIG. 55.—Determination of the date of crossing a temperature threshold

Number of Occasions of Certain Phenomena

The isopleth method is suitable for the demonstration of discontinuous phenomena such as days with snowfall, days with thunder, days with frost, &c. Abundant data for such exercises are contained in the tables in the *Handbuch der Klimatologie*. The construction of maps showing such frequencies presents no difficulties, but the picture they give is often illuminating.

Ex. Table 20 gives the number of days with frost in (pre-war) Germany. Inspection of the columns conveys only a confused impression. An isopleth map based on the plotted figures reveals a clear

TABLE 20: *Days with frost in Germany*

Schlesvig	. . .	83	Posen	. . . .	96	Arnsberg . . .	85
Sylt .	. . .	73	Köslin	. . . .	114	Frankfurt on Main	68
Heligoland .	. .	54	Dantzig	. . . .	95	Fulda	99
Meldorf	. . .	89	Thorn	. . . .	116	Geisenheim . .	84
Borkum	. . .	53	Königsberg	. .	111	Wiesbaden . . .	68
Emden .	. . .	71	Margrabawa	. .	145	Ansbach . . .	120
Oldenburg .	. .	84	Insterburg .	. .	128	Bayreuth . . .	105
Bremen	. . .	78	Deutschkrone .	.	111	Nürnberg . . .	105
Osnabrück .	. .	73	Hela		90	Regensberg . .	112
Münster	. . .	86	Konitz		124	Würtzberg . . .	88
Krefeld .	. . .	65	Frankfurt on Oder		98	Augsberg . . .	110
Köln	. . .	54	Landsberg on			Landshut . . .	130
Aachen .	. . .	62	Warthe . . .		110	München . . .	113
Koblenz	. . .	73	Koslin		114	Passau	104
Trier	. . .	73	Lauenburg . .		120	Kaiserlautern . .	93
			Putbus		90		
Wiesbaden .	. .	70				Bautzen . . .	89
Marburg	. . .	105	Swinemünde . .		81	Chemnitz . . .	98
Kassel .	. . .	83	Bromberg . . .		108	Freudenstadt . .	131
Hanover	. . .	70	Franstadt . . .		102	Friedrichshafen .	103
Kiel		86	Beuthen . . .		117	Heidenheim . .	126
			Breslau		98		
Hamburg .	. .	71				Heilbronn . . .	84
Celle	. . .	90	Glatz		124	Stuttgart . . .	73
Erfurt .	. . .	111	Görlitz		94	Ulm	124
Bamberg	. .	109	Grünberg . . .		101	Karlsruhe . . .	80
Halle .	. . .	82	Oppeln		103	Hochenschwand .	142
			Ratibor . . .		105		
Leipzig .	. . .	87				Darmstadt . . .	75
Magdeburg	. .	84	Schreiberhau . .		150	Mainz	68
Lübeck .	. . .	86	Gardelegen . .		91	Michelstadt . .	115
Schwerin	. .	88	Nordhausen . .		92	Neustrelitz . . .	105
Rostock .	. . .	96	Torgau		89	Jena	106
			Flensburg . . .		76		
Stettin .	. . .	95				Koburg	110
Berlin .	. . .	79	Gramm		105	Meiningen . . .	99
Dresden	. . .	75	Göttingen . . .		83	Sonderhausen . .	98
Liegnitz	. . .	103	Klausthal . . .		137	Birkenfeld . . .	116
Breslau .	. . .	100	Lüneburg . . .		91	Braunschweig . .	82
			Osnabrück . . .		74		

pattern, whose explanation calls for an appreciation of the factors involved. The locating of the stations from a gazetteer and atlas may advance one's knowledge of the geography of Germany.

Diurnal and Annual Incidence of Phenomena

Ex. The data given below may be made into a cartogram (cf. pp. 121 and 136), from which a good deal can be learnt.

TABLE 21: *Total number of occasions on which thunder was recorded between 1889 and 1908 at Curityba, Brazil*

Hours	J.	F.	M.	A.	M.	J.	Jy.	A.	S.	O.	N.	D.
0– 2	13	11	10	7	20	12	7	29	27	31	11	15
2– 4	8	7	4	5	24	12	11	27	32	30	12	7
4– 6	6	4	0	3	17	14	12	28	35	27	10	4
6– 8	4	4	2	4	8	17	9	26	32	27	4	3
8–10	1	2	0	7	7	10	7	29	28	24	8	4
10–12	11	8	6	5	9	12	2	30	22	24	15	15
12–14	69	54	31	9	14	7	2	29	29	42	36	66
14–16	135	86	77	25	13	16	9	21	29	55	60	96
16–18	126	94	86	24	12	16	8	25	44	49	54	79
18–20	73	68	43	10	15	16	12	33	36	40	36	62
20–22	39	43	23	16	15	11	11	30	29	28	27	31
22–24	20	15	15	7	15	9	11	31	20	15	20	16

With such a 'chancy' phenomenon as thunder the pattern is not quite so clearly defined, nor the gradations so regular as in the two previous diagrams of sunshine and temperature.

CHAPTER 5

THE WATER CIRCULATION:
RAINFALL AND HYDROLOGY

RAINFALL, together with other forms of precipitation (collectively
called hydrometeors), is, of course, an element of climate, but the
subsequent movements of water derived from this source are the concern of hydrology. There is a continuous circulation consisting of
descent (as rain), re-evaporation, ascent (as water vapour), condensation (as cloud), descent (as rain). It seems desirable, therefore, to consider rainfall as part of the hydrographic cycle, the main ramifications
of which are illustrated diagrammatically in Fig. 56.

Section I. Ingestion. The Analysis of Precipitation

Precipitation

Whether in the form of rain, snow, or hail, precipitation is stated
in the equivalent depth of water accumulated. The gradations of
quantity over the surface of the earth are not necessarily continuous
and there need not be, for example, a place with 20 in. between one
with 21 and another with 19. In practice, however, its distribution can
be satisfactorily represented by isohyets which always fall into a rational
pattern, especially when long-term averages are under consideration.

The 'annual march' of rainfall, unlike that of temperature, is not
a smooth progression by fairly regular steps from month to month, but
is in many places interrupted by sudden discontinuities. The year-
to-year variation of monthly or annual totals is also much greater
than that of, say, temperature, and mean values are much less reliable
and representative. The analysis of its variability thus becomes an
important matter, especially as rain has such a vital importance for
man and his crops. On the other hand critical values are not so sharply
marked, there is no clearly defined change-point, and though there is
such a thing as 'disastrous deficiency', it differs from 'just sufficiency'
less abruptly than, for example, frost from thaw, or rain from snow (a
temperature difference).

The Utilization of Short-Period Rainfall Records

The task of preparing a map of average rainfall over a relatively
small region usually confronts the geographer with the problem of
short-period records. It is generally considered that 35 years is the

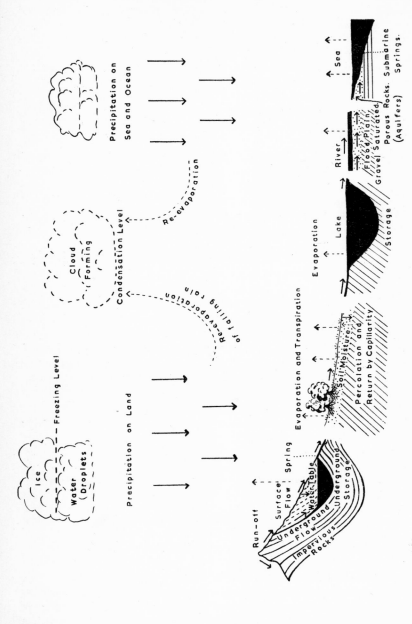

FIG. 56.—Hydrographic cycle

minimum period required to give a reasonably steady value for the average annual rainfall at any station, but not all stations in a given region are likely to have records of this length. However, those with shorter records can also contribute to the rainfall map through simple methods of computing 35-year averages. These are based on the reasonable assumption that rainfall variations at different stations in the same region (e.g. a river basin) bear fairly constant ratios one to the other.

A method used by the Meteorological Office is described in an article by Dr. J. Glasspoole entitled 'The Rainfall of Norfolk', published in *British Rainfall*, 1928. The procedure, slightly modified, is as follows (see Table 22).

1. Tabulate all the complete (i.e. standard 35-year period) records of stations in the region. (Cols. 2, 3, and 4.)
2. Average the annual amounts at these stations to give a general average for each year. (Col. 5.)
3. Find the mean general average for the 35-year period, and express each annual figure as a percentage of this mean. (Col. 6.)
4. For each station with a short-period record, find the mean rainfall for that period.
5. By reference to the general percentage for that short period, increase or decrease the short-period mean to give a computed 35-year mean for each station.

Ex. Table 22 gives annual rainfall figures for certain stations in the Reading area: three have complete records, and the rest have short records ranging from 3 to 14 years. (The period taken here is 1916–50, which will eventually become the standard period for rainfall averages, replacing 1881–1915, which is still officially used at present.)

Consider the short-period record for Waverley Road: the mean for this record is 31·00 in. At the University, Caversham Lock, and Bath Road Waterworks, the general percentage of the mean, for the same period, is 116. It is assumed, in other words, that for the whole of the Reading area the rainfall of the period 1925–6–7 was 116 per cent. of normal. Thus, for Waverley Road, the computed 35-year mean is

$$31{\cdot}00 \times \frac{100}{116} = 26{\cdot}72$$

Essentially the same method is described by V. Conrad (in *Methods in Climatology*, Harvard University Press, 1950), again based on the principle of constant ratios. A station X with a complete 35-year record has an average rainfall x_{35}, and a second station Y, in the same region, has been operating for only n years (within the 35-year period), for which the average rainfall is Y_n. The corresponding average at X for

Table 22: *Rainfall records in the Reading area*
(Annual aggregates in inches)

1 Year	2 University	3 Caversham Lock	4 Bath Rd. Water Works	5 General Average	6 % of Mean	7 Waverley Road	8 Seed Trial Grounds	9 Kidmore End School	10 Northcourt Avenue	11 Victoria Sq.	12 Sonning Deanery
1916	32·80	29·95	33·03					37·91	32·24	33·87	
17	26·52	23·50	25·70					28·25	27·06	27·36	
18	28·80	24·18	27·54					33·47	27·96	29·25	
19	28·44	23·28	28·27					30·94	28·65	29·17	
20	26·95	24·70	25·24					35·39	24·59	26·77	
1921	15·89	12·62	14·69					18·58		15·61	
22	25·28	22·55	24·05					31·87		25·70	
23	27·82	23·30	26·94					32·64			
24	31·91	30·89	30·75	28·75	115	30·43		38·79			
25	29·70	28·12	28·42					33·93			
1926	25·89	23·48	25·16					26·05			24·20
27	33·78	32·20	33·72	24·84	99	26·47		37·02			23·10
28	25·20	24·36	25·28	33·23	133	36·11		29·91			19·04
29	22·92	21·23	22·01					24·94			21·77
30	24·49	22·04	24·77								26·19
1931	24·59	21·93	23·91								27·49
32	24·99	22·65	24·47								28·95
33	20·42	19·87	20·84								
34	22·21	20·71	21·70				28·97				
35	28·87	28·09	29·58				24·19				
1936	28·43	27·94	29·09								
37	29·86	29·05	30·01								
38	20·42	19·29	20·41								
39	30·33	30·10	28·91								
40	25·49	24·93	24·48								
1941	26·57	26·70	27·50				25·99				
42	22·74	22·70	23·49				22·01				
43	21·15	21·01	21·81				19·98				
44	19·89	20·45	20·31				18·84				
45	21·99	21·60	21·23				20·43				
1946	29·11	29·20	27·98				29·05				
47	18·96	19·08	18·51				17·59				
48	25·10	24·91	24·69				22·65				
49	22·87	21·91	23·83				21·45				
50	28·54	27·29	28·36				26·29				
Mean				25·07							

the same short period is x. Then the computed 35-year average at Y, i.e. y_{35}, is given by

$$\frac{x_{35}}{y_{35}} = \frac{x_n}{y_n}$$

If X is taken to represent not merely one station but all available stations with complete records, more reliable results will clearly be obtained.

In the case of Waverley Road, where $y_3 = 31 \cdot 00$, x_{35} (X representing University, Caversham Lock, and Bath Road) $= 25 \cdot 07$, and $x_3 = 28 \cdot 94$,

$$y_{35} = \frac{25 \cdot 07 \times 31 \cdot 00}{28 \cdot 94} = 26 \cdot 85$$

Whichever version of the method is used, a 3-year record is probably the shortest which will give reasonable results, while obviously enough, the longer the record, the more reliable is the computed value.

Ex. The student may complete the exercise by computing mean values for the five remaining stations in Table 22.

Rainfall: Mean, Mode, and Median

Ex. Table 23 gives the monthly and yearly totals of rainfall at Alexandria for the 35 years from 1896 to 1930.

Consider first the yearly totals and calculate—

1. The arithmetic *mean* which is adopted for climatic statistics.
2. The *mode* or most frequently recurring amount. For this purpose we subdivide the record into bands of convenient width, say 10 mm., and arrange them in a column of descending order of magnitude. We then count up the number of occasions on which the precipitation has fallen within each of these bands. The band with the largest number of occurrences is the mode. It will be found that there is no regular increase towards the mode and decrease away from it. In fact, the position of the mode is indefinite and difficult to determine; there may be two or more modes.
3. The *median* or middle value. To determine this the 35 yearly figures are arranged in a column of descending order of magnitude. The 18th figure from top or bottom is the median, which gives the average expectation of rain, half the years being wetter and half drier than it. Since the variation below the median is limited by zero while the upward variation is unlimited, the latter nearly always exceed the former and the median is generally less than the mean, which gives, therefore, a flattering picture of the annual rainfall.

TABLE 23: *Alexandria (Kôm el Nadura), Egypt*

Lat. 31° 12′ N. Long. 29° 53′ E. Height 32 m.
Precipitation in millimetres—Totals

Date	J.	F.	M.	A.	M.	J.	Jy.	A.	S.	O.	N.	D.	Total for year
1896	69	45	19	2	0	0	0	0	1	1	43	28	208
97	127	12	14	0	0	0	0	0	0	14	52	107	326
98	57	47	6	0	0	0	0	0	0	0	60	144	314
99	72	23	3	0	0	0	0	0	0	58	25	64	245
1900	14	33	16	1	2	0	0	0	0	0	10	126	202
1901	113	3	4	0	6	0	0	0	11	0	31	57	225
02	104	8	4	6	1	0	0	0	0	5	40	90	258
03	90	34	14	0	0	0	0	0	0	0	10	24	172
04	63	12	1	2	0	0	0	0	0	3	65	50	196
05	46	16	14	0	0	0	0	0	0	28	7	159	270
1906	32	43	6	3	9	0	0	0	0	19	64	31	207
07	25	13	38	7	0	0	0	2	0	0	50	25	160
08	80	47	14	3	0	1	0	0	0	0	39	76	260
09	43	41	0	51	0	0	0	0	0	21	22	31	209
10	86	8	19	2	3	0	0	0	4	0	30	28	180
1911	28	42	12	2	0	0	0	0	0	8	17	79	188
12	21	24	9	0	2	0	0	0	0	0	10	27	93
13	12	36	21	0	0	0	0	0	0	14	79	98	260
14	28	31	7	8	0	0	0	0	0	0	29	103	206
15	19	19	19	1	0	0	0	0	0	0	14	10	82
1916	109	14	8	2	0	0	0	0	0	0	21	45	199
17	66	39	13	1	0	0	0	0	0	8	8	65	200
18	39	31	6	0	0	0	0	0	0	0	53	50	179
19	36	4	1	0	0	0	0	0	0	3	54	126	224
20	35	42	11	0	0	0	0	0	0	0	6	39	133
1921	23	20	57	0	9	0	0	0	0	9	23	42	183
22	63	5	3	0	0	0	0	0	0	0	10	106	187
23	17	19	2	0	0	0	0	0	0	5	0	62	105
24	80	48	0	0	0	0	0	0	0	9	55	78	270
25	106	10	14	4	0	0	0	0	0	2	20	30	186
1926	16	28	17	9	0	0	0	0	0	0	7	88	165
27	30	72	5	6	0	0	0	0	0	0	168	29	310
28	17	30	8	0	0	0	0	0	0	0	28	16	99
29	79	28	2	13	0	0	0	0	0	6	35	85	248
1930	92	21	0	0	0	0	0	0	0	20	25	37	195

4. *The Upper and Lower Quartiles.* These are the mid-points between the median and the upper and lower extremes of rainfall, i.e. the 9th values from top and bottom of the descending magnitude column. The inter-quartile range, enclosing half the recorded values, clearly gives the 50 per cent. expectation of rain.

5. *The Upper and Lower Octiles.* These are the mid-points between

the Quartile and the extreme. The inter-octile range clearly gives the 75 per cent. expectation of rain.

Ex. *The Dispersion Diagram.* Draw a horizontal line on graph paper and divide into twelve equal parts for the months. Choose a convenient vertical scale for rainfall and using the data in Table 23 place dots representing the amount of rain in each month in each year. Except in months where nil rainfall occurs there will clearly be 35 dots in each column. Where the same value occurs twice in the month the dots should be placed side by side, otherwise they should be arranged on a vertical line in the middle of the column. Mark the position of the monthly medians, quartiles, and octiles and lightly shade the inter-quartile range.

This dispersion diagram, like Fig. 53, gives a clear picture, easily appreciated by the eye, of the way in which the rain happens. At this stage it is entirely pictorial, but it lends itself to quantitative analysis, as will be shown below.[1]

Rainfall Discontinuities and Monthly Rainfall Differences

According to P. R. Crowe a 'major discontinuity' exists where, in any two months undergoing comparison, the lower quartile of one month lies above the upper quartile of the other. A 'minor discontinuity' exists where the median and lower quartile of one month lie above the upper quartile and median respectively of the other month. Such discontinuities are symptomatic of a very real difference in meteorological conditions and indicate the sudden appearance or departure of some rain-producing condition, e.g. the burst of the monsoon. They show up very clearly on the dispersion diagram, and, when well marked, may often be detected by mere inspection of the monthly precipitation figures, but they are more clearly distinguished if we list the differences between adjacent months thus:

J.	F.	M.	A.	M.	J.	Jy.	A.	S.	O.	N.	D.	Lahore
0·9	1·0	0·8	0·5	0·7	1·4	5·1	4·7	2·3	0·3	0·1	0·4	Precipitation
+·6	+·1	−·2	−·3	+·2	+·7	+3·7	−·4	−2·4	−2·0	−·2	+·3	Diff. from previous month
225	111	80	62	140	200	364	92	49	13	33	400	% of previous month

[1] See also: P. R. Crowe, 'The Analysis of Rainfall Probability', *Scot. Geog. Mag.*, 1933; and H. A. Matthews, 'A New View of some Familiar Indian Rainfalls', *Scot. Geog. Mag.*, 1936.

The differences bring out very clearly the onset of the monsoon in July (and probably the end of June) and its more gradual departure in September and October. Closer inspection reveals the appearance of the light cyclonic rains in January. The third line shows the rainfall expressed as a percentage of that of the previous month and exposes the obvious weakness of such a method when applied to small values of no real significance, e.g. December.

Variability of Rainfall

Ex. The Alexandria figures (yearly total) may be used again for this exercise.

1. Construct a block graph of the 35 yearly totals.
2. Construct a line graph centred on the normal, showing the departures above and below the normal. This will be found more revealing.
3. Calculate the average for each 5-year period and plot these as a block graph.
4. Calculate the 5-yearly running average (1896–1900, 1897–1901, 1898–1902, &c.) and plot these as a line graph—centred on the normal. It will smooth out the sudden changes in graph 2.
5. Express the departure from the normal for each year as a percentage of the normal. The mean of these, ignoring the sign, is the 'mean variability'. It is naturally much larger for arid than for humid stations. Calculate and compare the mean variability for January (a wet month) and October (a dry month).
6. How many years are wetter than the normal and what is their mean variability?
7. How many are drier than the normal and what is their mean variability? Compare and comment upon the variability of wet and dry years.

Seasonal Distribution of Rainfall

Figures are provided (in Table 24) of the monthly rainfall averages for European and Mediterranean stations.

Ex. 1. Group the months into seasons in the conventional way—

i.e. Dec. + Jan. + Feb. = Winter 90¼ days
  Mar. + Apr. + May = Spring 92 days
  Jun. + Jul. + Aug. = Summer 92 days
  Sept. + Oct. + Nov. = Autumn 91 days

Consider one season at a time and for each station calculate the percentage of the total yearly rainfall occurring in this season. Plot

TABLE 24: *Régime of rainfall, Europe and the Mediterranean*

Rainfall in Inches

Station	J.	F.	Total	%	P.C.	M.	A.	M.	Total	%	P.C.	J.	Jy.	A.	Total	%	P.C.	S.	O.	N.	Total	%	P.C.	D.	Total
Lisbon	3·6	3·5				3·4	2·6	2·0				0·8	0·2	0·2				1·4	3·3	4·3				4·1	29·4
Gibraltar	5·1	4·2				4·8	2·7	1·7				0·5	—	0·1				1·4	3·3	6·4				5·5	35·7
Morocco	1·3	1·2				1·4	1·1	0·7				0·3	0·2	—				0·3	0·5	1·5				0·9	9·4
Mogador	2·2	1·5				2·2	0·7	0·6				0·1	—	—				0·2	1·3	2·4				2·0	13·2
Algiers	4·2	3·5				3·5	2·3	1·3				0·6	0·1	0·3				1·1	3·1	4·6				5·4	30·0
Marseilles	1·7	1·4				1·9	2·2	1·7				1·1	0·7	0·8				2·4	3·8	2·8				2·1	22·6
Rome	3·2	2·7				2·9	2·6	2·2				1·6	0·7	1·0				2·5	5·0	4·4				3·9	32·7
Palermo	3·2	2·7				2·8	1·9	1·1				0·7	0·2	0·4				1·8	3·2	3·3				3·6	25·0
Athens	2·0	1·7				1·2	0·9	0·8				0·7	0·3	0·5				0·6	1·6	2·6				2·6	15·5
Alexandria	2·2	0·9				0·5	0·2	—				—	—	—				—	0·3	1·4				2·6	8·1
Smyrna	4·3	3·3				3·2	1·7	1·3				0·6	0·1	—				0·7	1·7	3·6				5·2	25·7
Jerusalem	6·2	4·6				3·5	1·5	0·3				—	—	—				—	0·4	2·5				5·7	24·7
Valencia	5·5	5·2				4·5	3·7	3·2				3·2	3·8	4·8				4·1	5·6	5·5				6·6	55·7
Aberdeen	2·2	2·1				2·4	1·9	2·3				1·7	2·8	2·7				2·2	3·0	3·0				3·2	29·5
Brest	2·6	2·4				2·2	2·1	2·4				1·5	1·3	1·9				2·5	3·4	3·1				3·7	29·1
Paris	1·5	1·4				1·6	1·7	1·9				2·1	2·2	2·1				1·9	2·3	1·9				2·0	22·6
Berlin	1·7	1·4				1·6	1·5	1·9				2·3	3·0	2·3				1·7	1·7	1·7				1·9	22·7
Milan	2·4	2·3				2·7	3·4	4·1				3·3	2·8	3·2				3·5	4·7	4·3				3·0	39·8
Breslau	1·3	1·0				1·6	1·5	2·4				2·4	3·4	2·8				2·0	1·5	1·5				1·5	22·9
Vienna	1·5	1·3				1·8	2·0	2·8				2·7	3·1	2·7				2·0	1·9	1·8				1·8	25·4
Warsaw	1·2	1·1				1·3	1·5	1·9				2·6	3·0	2·9				1·9	1·6	1·5				1·5	22·1
Belgrade	1·2	1·3				1·6	2·3	2·8				3·2	2·7	1·9				1·7	2·2	1·7				1·7	24·4
Bukarest	1·3	1·1				1·6	1·7	2·5				3·5	2·7	2·0				1·6	1·7	1·9				1·6	23·1
Kiev	1·1	0·8				1·5	1·7	1·7				2·4	3·0	2·4				1·7	1·7	1·5				1·5	21·0
Odessa	0·9	0·7				1·1	1·1	1·3				2·3	2·1	1·2				1·4	1·1	1·6				1·3	16·0

Station													
Vestmannö	5·8	4·8	4·4	3·8	3·2	3·3	3·1	3·1	5·7	5·8	5·3	5·5	53·8
Thorshavn	6·7	5·3	4·9	3·7	3·3	2·6	3·2	3·6	4·7	6·1	6·5	6·6	57·2
Bergen	9·0	6·6	6·2	4·3	4·7	4·1	5·7	7·8	9·2	9·3	8·5	8·9	84·3
Trondheim	4·3	3·0	3·4	2·5	2·2	1·9	2·8	3·4	4·4	5·0	3·9	3·4	40·2
Bodö	3·3	2·7	2·3	2·0	2·0	2·1	2·6	3·0	4·5	4·0	4·0	3·1	35·5
Copenhagen	1·5	1·3	1·4	1·4	1·5	2·0	2·4	2·6	2·1	2·2	1·9	1·7	22·0
Upsala	1·3	1·1	1·2	1·2	1·7	2·0	2·7	2·8	2·0	2·1	1·7	1·6	21·4
Königsberg	1·7	1·4	1·5	1·5	2·0	2·4	3·4	3·5	3·0	2·4	2·3	2·3	27·4
Haparanda	1·5	1·1	1·0	1·0	1·2	1·5	1·8	2·1	2·4	2·2	2·0	1·4	19·2
Helsinki	1·8	1·4	1·4	1·4	1·8	1·8	2·2	2·9	2·5	2·6	2·5	2·4	24·7
Leningrad	1·0	0·9	0·9	1·0	1·6	2·0	2·5	2·8	2·1	1·8	1·4	1·2	19·3
Moscow	1·1	0·9	1·2	1·5	1·9	2·0	2·8	2·9	2·2	1·4	1·6	1·5	21·0
Archangel	0·9	0·7	0·8	0·7	1·2	1·8	2·4	2·4	2·2	1·6	1·2	0·9	16·8
Kazan	0·5	0·4	0·6	0·9	1·6	2·2	2·4	2·4	1·6	1·1	1·0	0·7	15·4
Orenburg	1·1	0·8	1·0	0·9	1·4	2·0	1·7	1·3	1·3	1·2	1·2	1·2	15·2
Glasgow	3·3	2·9	2·7	2·1	2·6	2·5	3·1	3·9	3·0	3·4	3·6	4·1	37·2
Cambridge	1·5	1·3	1·5	1·3	1·8	2·1	2·2	2·3	1·6	2·4	1·9	1·9	21·8
Scilly	3·0	2·6	2·4	1·9	1·7	1·7	2·2	2·6	2·4	3·7	3·3	4·4	31·9
Lille	2·0	1·6	1·9	1·6	2·2	2·2	2·7	2·4	2·5	3·1	2·4	2·4	27·0
Bordeaux	2·5	2·0	2·3	2·5	2·8	2·8	1·9	2·0	2·6	3·6	3·1	2·7	30·7
Lyon	1·5	1·5	1·9	2·4	3·3	3·3	3·0	3·2	3·0	3·9	2·6	1·7	31·3
Metz	1·9	1·5	1·8	1·7	2·0	2·7	2·9	2·4	2·6	2·8	2·2	2·2	25·8
Brussels	2·2	1·9	2·0	1·9	2·3	2·5	2·9	3·0	2·6	2·8	2·5	2·4	28·9
Hamburg	2·0	1·7	2·1	1·8	2·0	2·4	3·5	3·1	2·2	2·6	2·0	2·2	27·5
Hanover	1·7	1·5	2·1	1·6	2·1	2·7	3·3	2·8	1·9	2·0	1·7	1·8	25·2
Frankfurt	1·5	1·3	1·7	1·2	2·0	2·2	2·7	2·3	1·9	2·1	1·7	2·0	22·7
Geneva	1·6	1·8	2·1	2·6	3·2	3·0	3·1	3·5	3·1	4·4	3·1	2·2	33·7
Madrid	1·3	1·1	1·7	1·9	1·7	1·2	0·5	0·4	1·3	1·8	1·9	1·6	16·4
Budapest	1·5	1·3	1·8	2·4	2·8	3·0	2·1	2·0	2·1	2·5	1·9	1·9	25·9
Sofia	1·5	1·4	1·5	2·0	3·4	3·2	2·7	2·1	1·9	2·4	1·9	1·4	25·9

Rainfall in Inches

Station	J.	F.	Total	%	P.C.	M.	A.	M.	Total	%	P.C.	J.	Jy.	A.	Total	%	P.C.	S.	O.	N.	Total	%	P.C.	D.	Total
Istanbul	3·4	2·7				2·4	1·7	1·2				1·3	1·1	1·7				2·0	2·5	4·0				4·8	28·9
Sivas	2·1	1·7				1·4	2·3	3·0				1·1	0·4	0·1				0·7	1·2	1·9				0·9	16·9
Tiflis	0·6	0·8				1·1	2·1	2·9				2·7	2·1	1·6				2·0	1·3	1·1				0·8	19·1
Batum	10·2	6·0				6·2	5·0	2·8				5·9	6·0	8·2				11·9	8·8	12·2				10·0	93·3
Astrakhan	0·5	0·3				0·4	0·5	0·6				0·7	0·5	0·5				0·5	0·4	0·4				0·5	5·9
Perm	1·5	1·2				1·1	1·1	2·0				2·7	2·8	2·9				2·3	1·9	2·0				1·7	23·2
Tripoli	3·3	1·8				0·9	0·5	0·3				0·1	0	0				0·5	1·8	2·4				4·7	16·3
Mersifun	0·8	1·0				1·9	2·0	2·7				2·6	0·7	0·8				1·0	1·2	1·3				1·3	17·3
Genoa	4·2	4·2				4·1	4·1	3·5				2·8	1·7	2·4				5·0	7·8	7·5				4·8	52·0
Trieste	2·2	2·3				2·8	2·9	3·7				4·1	3·7	3·7				4·0	4·7	3·6				3·4	41·8
Florence	2·7	2·5				3·0	3·1	3·1				2·2	1·4	2·0				3·3	4·3	4·0				3·2	34·8
Naples	3·5	2·8				2·9	2·6	2·0				1·3	0·6	1·1				2·8	4·5	4·6				4·4	33·0
Ragusa	6·8	5·0				5·4	4·8	3·5				2·8	1·3	2·6				4·3	7·7	7·8				7·2	59·2
Corfu	5·9	6·7				3·4	3·3	2·3				1·3	0·4	0·9				2·9	5·8	6·3				8·3	47·9
Salonika	1·5	1·4				1·6	1·9	2·4				1·7	1·0	1·2				1·6	2·1	2·7				2·4	21·5

these percentages on an outline map and interpolate isopleths. The isopleth interval should not be too small or difficulty will be experienced in their disposition; an interval of about 5 per cent. is quite smal enough.

The finished map should be carefully studied and the distribution related to such factors as pressure, marine influence, prevailing winds, and depression tracks. Similar maps may be constructed for the other seasons, but there is an alternative method that may be tried.

2. The Equipluve method. This, like the percentage method described above, may be applied to monthly or seasonal totals. The spring quarter contains 92 days. Therefore, if the rain were perfectly evenly distributed throughout the year, spring should receive $\frac{92}{365}$ of the total yearly rain. For practical purposes this can be considered as $\frac{1}{4}$, the error created thereby will be small, and will, moreover, apply equally to all stations. Divide the yearly rainfall at each station by 4 and express the spring total as a percentage of this quotient. The figure arrived at is known as the pluviometric coefficient. Lines joining places with the same P.C. are called equipluves. Plot the equipluves for spring, summer, autumn, and winter.

3. Map of wettest months. Here the inequality in length of the month is capable of introducing an error and it is advisable first to correct for this. This can be done *either* (converting to a 30-day month) by adding $\frac{1}{15}$ to the February rainfall and subtracting $\frac{1}{31}$ from the 31-day months *or*, more quickly if less exactly (converting to a 31-day month) by adding 10 per cent. to the February figures and 3 per cent. to April, June, September, and November. On the outline map write the initial letters (or the number, 1–12) of the month of heaviest rainfall on the site of each station. Draw boundary lines dividing the continent into regions characterized by having their heaviest rainfall in the same month. Examine the map carefully and explain the facts brought to light. Such a map can be seen in Bartholomew's *Meteorological Atlas*, plate 19.

Evaporation (*Direct Measurement*)

The measurement of evaporation is beset with difficulties. Standard tanks are used which may be said to give a measure of evaporation from a free water surface, but this does not, of course, tally with the

San Antonio, Texas (inches)	J.	F.	M.	A.	M.	J.	Jy.	A.	S.	O.	N.	D.	Year
1. Precipitation	1·4	1·6	1·7	3·1	3·2	2·4	2·1	2·3	3·0	2·2	1·8	1·6	26·4
2. Evaporation	2·4	3·0	4·5	5·5	6·6	7·9	9·1	9·1	6·8	5·0	3·1	2·4	65·4
3. Difference													
4. Tank level													

actual loss of water by evaporation from the ground, plus transpiration from plants.

Ex. Although San Antonio has quite a good rainfall the accumulation of rain could not keep pace with evaporation loss either in the wettest summer month or the coolest month when evaporation is least. Complete line 3 and enter, on line 4, the level at the end of each month in an exposed water tank filled to a depth of four feet on New Year's Day.

TABLE 25: *Evaporation at Harrogate (Yorks.)*

Year	1943	1944	1945	1946	1947	1948
Jan.	0·49	0·41	0·18	0·33	0·23	0·37
Feb.	0·67	0·41	0·20	0·40	0·25	0·40
Mar.	1·19	0·87	1·51	0·62	0·23	1·04
Apr.	2·36	1·89	2·04	1·92	2·17	1 99
May	2·99	2·61	2·93	2·84	2·92	2·88
Jun.	3·21	3·32	3·50	2·79	2·74	2·85
Jul.	3·36	2·64	3·50	3·12	3·33	2·83
Aug.	2·53	3·00	2·65	2·47	3·13	2·15
Sep.	1·94	1·72	1·84	1·55	2·37	1·65
Oct.	0·93	1·47	0·96	1·13	0·87	1·23
Nov.	0·71	1·16	0·47	0·88	0·92	0·52
Dec.	0·41	0·51	0·34	0·39	0·28	0·38
Year	20·79	20·01	20·12	18·44	19·44	18·32
Average 1908–42	19·53					
Diff.	+ 1·26	+ 0·52	+ 0·59	− 1·09	− 0·09	− 1·21

and Petersfield (Hants)

Year	1943	1944	1945	1946	1947	1948
Jan.	0·09	0·14	0·00	0·13	0·00	0·02
Feb.	0·28	0·70	0·05	0·16	0·20	0·16
Mar.	1·04	1·15	1·01	0·73	0·25	1·31
Apr.	2·06	1·93	2·28	1·97	1·74	2·22
May	3·19	3·09	2·25	3·02	2·45	3·65
Jun.	3·39	3·39	2·84	2·46	3·67	2·94
Jul.	3·03	2·24	3·24	3·89	3·58	3·04
Aug.	2·75	2·80	2·40	2·34	4·22	2·29
Sep.	1·67	1·66	1·24	1·22	2·13	1·61
Oct.	0·82	0·99	0·78	1·08	1·06	0·98
Nov.	0·33	0·27	0·38	0·41	0·22	0·26
Dec.	0·02	0·00	0·09	0·20	0·10	0·00
Year	18·67	18·36	16·56	17·61	19·62	18·48
Average 1908–42	17·00					
Diff.	+ 1·67	+ 1·36	− 0·44	+ 0·61	+ 2·62	+ 1·48

Ex. Table 25 gives six years of evaporation figures for Harrogate and Petersfield. The year-to-year variation may be analysed by the methods applied on pp. 131 and 142 and to those used in the analysis of variability of rainfall on p. 155.

The number of stations keeping records of evaporation is small and the results are not yet entirely satisfactory. It is therefore commonly done to estimate evaporation, on either theoretical or empirical grounds, from combinations of other elements (e.g. temperature and rainfall). Further consideration of evaporation will, therefore, be postponed until the methods of analysing combinations of elements have been studied.

Section II. Metabolism. The Function of Water

Comparison of Two Variables

Two variables can be compared, and often are, by graphing each separately and placing the two graphs side by side, or one above the other or by superimposing them. The result is generally confusion unless the correspondence is so obvious as to need no graph to examine and detect it. The figures given on p. 167 (July rainfall and yield of corn in Ohio) may be used to demonstrate the futility of such graphs. If the two sets of figures are plotted in chronological order on the same line, one in red and the other in black, it will be found impossible from an inspection of the zigzag lines to detect, in more than general terms, any coincidence between peaks or troughs. Block graphs would be clearer, but still not very satisfactory. It must be recognized that time, i.e. succession of years, is irrelevant in this connexion and the chronological order, which only obscures the relationship, must be abandoned.

Ex. One of the variables (preferably the causal factor, i.e. rainfall) should be rearranged in descending order of magnitude and plotted as a line declining to the right. The other variable (yield) should then be plotted on the same vertical line as the rainfall of the appropriate year. Both graphs should be centred on the same line, which should correspond with the mean value for each variable. Despite considerable fluctuations from year to year the general downward trend of yield with decreasing rainfall will now be apparent. A much better method of analysis will, however, be offered below (p. 166).

Combined Phenomena

Up to this last exercise we have generally been using graphical or cartographical methods to demonstrate or to analyse a single element of climate. On the graph we have used the vertical for the value of the element and the horizontal, generally, for time (hours, days, months, or years) or distance. If, now, we make use of the abscissae for a second element of climate, the factor of time or distance, whose irrelevance in most cases has just been demonstrated, can no longer be shown proceeding continuously in one direction; but some conventionalized diagrams can be constructed to give a picture, which, when the convention is recognized, can be informative. Simple examples are the quograph on p. 116, the climograph (Fig. 57), and the hythergraph (Fig. 58).

It will be noted that each of the 12 monthly points in these diagrams, as in the quograph, is a quotient; in the case of the hythergraph it is a temperature/rainfall ratio. But since no systematic relationship exists between temperature and rainfall the line (polygon) produced by joining up the 12 monthly points has an irregular form that defies analysis and is not one that can be expressed mathematically. But if

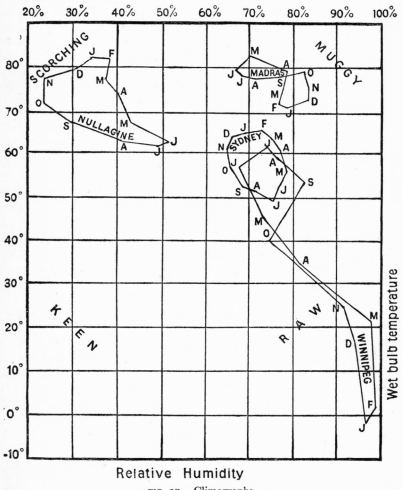

FIG. 57.—Climographs
(*After Griffith Taylr*)

a mathematical relationship does exist between the two variables shown on the co-ordinates then the points will fall on a line whose formula can be ascertained. This is, of course, a well-known device in the physical sciences and we may use, as an example, the following extract from the hygrometric tables (Table 26).

Ex. Using the dry-bulb temperature for the ordinates and the depression of the wet bulb as abscissae place a dot at each intersection and write the value of the dew-point; draw isopleths in full lines. Repeat for the relative humidity using dotted lines. The graph can then be used as a ready reckoner for the calculation of any one value from two of the others. Notice that it is immaterial which values are used as co-ordinates, though convenience of scale makes some more suitable

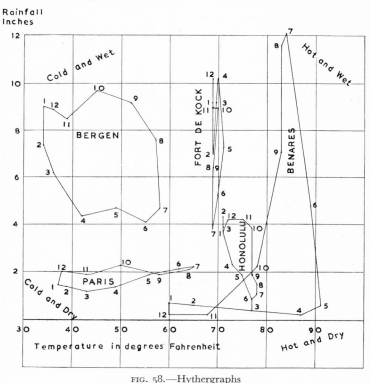

FIG. 58.—Hythergraphs

Figures on polygons refer to months, Jan. (1) to Dec. (12)

than others. The picture is tied together by a network of intersecting lines rigidly fixed by their constant interrelation.

Now since the method can be used to demonstrate the existence of a true relationship it can also be used to test whether a relationship exists between two 'variables', i.e. whether one is a 'function' of the other. Asked in this form the question is a direct invitation to use the method learnt in the mathematics class or the physics laboratory, but a request in some such form as 'examine the relationship between July rainfall and the yield of corn in Ohio' rarely receives the obvious

TABLE 26: *Relative humidity (%) and dew-point (° F.) at pressure = 30·0 in.*

Air temp. (dry bulb) t		Depression of wet-bulb thermometer (t − t')														
		1·0	2·0	3·0	4·0	5·0	6·0	7·0	8·0	9·0	10·0	11·0	12·0	13·0	14·0	15·0
20	D.P.	16	12	8	2	−7	−21									
	R.H.	85	70	55	40	26	12									
30	D.P.	27	25	21	18	14	8	+2	−7	−25						
	R.H.	89	78	67	56	46	36	26	16	6						
40	D.P.	38	35	33	30	28	25	21	18	13	7	−1	−14			
	R.H.	92	83	75	68	60	52	45	37	29	22	15	7			
50	D.P.	48	46	44	42	40	37	34	32	29	26	22	16	13	8	±0
	R.H.	93	87	80	74	67	61	55	49	43	38	32	27	21	16	10
60	D.P.	58	57	55	53	51	49	47	45	43	40	38	35	32	29	25
	R.H.	94	89	83	78	73	68	63	58	53	48	43	39	34	30	26
70	D.P.	69	67	65	64	62	61	59	57	55	53	51	49	47	44	42
	R.H.	95	90	86	81	77	72	68	64	59	55	51	48	44	40	36
80	D.P.	79	77	76	74	73	72	70	68	67	65	63	62	60	58	56
	R.H.	96	91	87	83	79	75	72	68	64	61	57	54	50	47	44

treatment it deserves. The applicability of a familiar mathematical method is often overlooked because the student is now 'doing geography'.

Ex. As a first trial of the method let us examine the frequency of different intensities of rain.

Plotting intensity against frequency, draw a separate curve for each of the five stations given in the table.

TABLE 27: *Frequency of rainfall of different intensities*

Station	Percentage number of days with falls not less than (in.):								
	0·04	0·2	0·4	0·6	0·8	1·0	1·2	1·6	2·0
Strontian (Argyll)	54·4	33·4	19·0	10·8	6·5	3·8	2·2	0·7	0·2
Glasgow	40·5	17·9	7·3	3·0	1·2	0·6	0·3	0·1	0·0
Scarborough	32·3	11·5	4·0	1·7	0·8	0·4	0·2	0·1	0·0
Falmouth	41·8	20·9	10·0	4·8	2·4	1·3	0·6	0·2	0·1
Dublin	35·4	12·2	4·2	1·9	0·9	0·5	0·3	0·1	0·0

It will be noted that though each station has its individual character they all demonstrate the steady falling off in frequency of wetter and wetter days. All points fall on a smooth curve, whose algebraic formula could be calculated.[1]

It will not escape notice that the figures given above are percentages derived from an enormous number of individual recordings over long periods of time. It would be possible, though very laborious, to plot each year separately; the graph would be spattered with dots, but the high intensities would be mainly in the rare frequencies and the low intensities in the high frequencies. A curve could then be drawn through the centre of mass of the dots and would look like the one already drawn.

Climate and Yield of Crops

For the geographical climatologist this is one of the commonest and most useful applications of the quograph principle. As a means of detecting relationships and of establishing quantitative correlations the procedure outlined below is vastly superior to the methods described on p. 162.

The success or failure of crops cannot often be attributed to a single cause, but it is frequently the case that one climatic element has a profound influence on the yield, and this particular influence can be examined graphically. We may use a scatter graph, like the one just mentioned, to examine the influence, if any, of the rainfall of July on the yield of corn in Ohio (Table 28); or in mathematical parlance, 'is yield a function of rainfall?'

[1] This is a good example of a graph that deserves the use of logarithmic paper.

The method is the same as that already used; with rainfall as ordinates and yield as abscissae place a dot corresponding to the yield and the rainfall of each year, as shown in Fig. 59.

If a relationship exists between the two variables the dots will be distributed in a more or less orderly way about a line, which may be straight or curved, and this line expresses their relationship algebraically. The more closely the dots lie to the line the closer is the relationship. If the dots are scattered haphazard and without plan then no relationship exists.

TABLE 28: *July rainfall and yield of corn in Ohio*

Year	Rainfall, in.	Yield, bushels	Year	Rainfall, in.	Yield, bushels
1854	2·6	26·0	1884	3·8	33·3
55	5·8	39·7	85	3·2	36·8
56	2·6	27·7	86	2·9	33·5
57	4·9	36·6	87	2·2	30·5
58	4·7	27·7	88	4·4	38·9
1859	1·6	29·5	1889	4·2	32·3
60	5·8	38·2	90	2·0	24·6
61	3·3	33·5	91	3·8	35·6
62	3·6	30·0	92	3·8	33·3
63	2·6	27·0	93	2·5	29·1
1864	2·1	27·0	1894	1·6	32·6
65	5·7	35·0	95	2·0	33·7
66	5·1	36·5	96	8·1	41·7
67	3·2	29·8	97	4·6	34·3
68	2·7	34·4	98	4·0	37·4
1869	4·8	28·4	1899	4·2	38·1
70	4·7	37·5	1900	4·6	42·6
71	3·7	36·7	01	2·7	30·0
72	6·7	40·9	02	4·7	38·8
73	6·2	35·1	03	3·7	31·5
1874	3·8	39·2	1904	4·1	32·8
75	6·9	34·2	05	3·9	37·9
76	6·4	36·9	06	5·1	42·2
77	3·7	32·5	07	5·4	34·8
78	5·4	37·8	08	4·1	36·1
1879	4·2	34·3	1909	3·8	38·7
80	4·2	38·9	10	3·2	36·6
81	3·6	31·0	11	2·4	38·6
82	3·2	34·0	12	5·7	42·8
83	4·2	24·2	13	5·2	37·8

Our next step is to determine the algebraic expression of the relationship. If this is required only in general terms it will be enough to draw the line by eye through the centre of the dots and we may ignore any that are very wide of the line, because this abnormality is probably

12

due to some outside influence affecting the yield in that year, e.g. blight or shortage of fertilizers. The general formula for a *straight* line is $y = a + bx$ where a and b are the constants to be determined. The formula can now be found by selecting any *two* points on the line and substituting the values of x and y read off on the graph.

The method is illustrated by Fig. 59. With the exception of two aberrant high yields and two unrepresentative drought years the dots

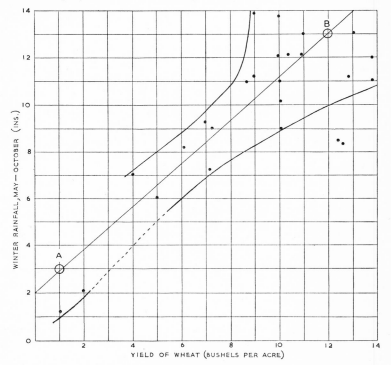

FIG. 59.—Winter rain and average yield of wheat in Victoria (Australia), 1890–1914. Formula of a straight line

are confined between the two curved lines between which is drawn a straight line AB, which expresses the relationship. The two points, A and B, have been selected for convenience at whole numbers on both scales.

The formula for a straight line is $y = a + bx$ or, in this particular case, Y (yield) $= a + b$ times R (the rainfall). We now have to find the value of the constants a and b. Substituting the values of Y and R at A on the graph we have the equation

$$1 = a + 3b \qquad . \qquad . \qquad . \qquad . \qquad \text{(i)}$$

similarly the point B gives

$$12 = a + 13\,b \qquad . \qquad . \qquad . \qquad . \qquad \text{(ii)}$$

subtracting i from ii 　　$11 = \qquad 10\,b$

hence 　　　　　　　$b = \dfrac{11}{10}$

Substituting this value for b in equation (i) we have

$$1 = a + 3\left(\frac{11}{10}\right)$$

$$a = 1 - \frac{33}{10}$$

$$a = -\,2\cdot3$$

i.e. the yield (in bushels) is approximately eleven-tenths of the rainfall (in inches) less 2·3 bushels per acre.

If the distribution of dots suggests not a straight line but a curve, parabola or hyperbola, the solution is much more difficult, involving elaborate mathematics and the determination of at least 3 constants. An example of such an equation is given by C. W. Thornthwaite (*Geog. Rev.*, 1948, p. 63) in which he shows that the optimum temperature for the growth of maize seedlings is 30° C. and that the relationship between growth rate and temperature is expressed by

$$V = \frac{449730\cdot7e^{24t}}{(e^{24t} + 1118\cdot8)^2}$$

when V is the growth rate as a percentage of the optimum, t is the temperature in degrees centigrade and e is the base of the Napierian system of logarithms. For non-mathematicians the expression of relationship is best left in the visual form as a curve from which probable yields for any rainfall can be read off by inspection.

The Method of Least Squares

If it is desired to establish the relationship between the two variables more precisely, we may, without drawing the graph at all, apply the method of least squares to the numerical data. To find b we use the formula

$$b = \frac{n(\Sigma\, RY) - (\Sigma\, R)\,(\Sigma Y)}{n(\Sigma\, R^2) - (\Sigma\, R)^2}$$

where n is the number of years, R is the rainfall and Y is the yield. We can find the sum of all the Rs and Ys and it will be necessary for each year to work out the value of Ry and R^2 and substitute these, summed, in the above equation.

Having thus determined the value of b, we can determine a by substitution in the equation

$$a = \frac{\Sigma y - b(\Sigma R)}{n}$$

A disadvantage of this algebraic method is that the final result is based upon *all* the data for *every* year, even the obviously aberrant ones in which no correlation exists. The ultimate expression of relationship may this be pulled out of true by what are probably chance operation of alien controls, perhaps biological (blight), economic (market prices), or even political (governmental interference). On the graph these could have been detected and, if not numerous, pruned out to give a tidier and truer expression of climatic control.

Ex. Table 29 supplies figures of the July temperature and the yield

TABLE 29: *Mean July temperature and yield of potatoes, Ohio. 1860–1914*

Year	Mean temp. July, ° F.	Bushels per acre	Year	Mean temp. July, ° F.	Bushels per acre
1860	73·2	84	1887	72·9	81
61	72·5	81	88	70·2	81
62	75·5	64	89	74·1	78
63	72·9	64			
64	74·5	69	1890	69·0	101
			91	72·0	86
1865	71·6	78	92	73·0	58
66	73·5	96	93	75·6	74
67	76·0	86	94	75·2	82
68	73·0	78			
69	75·2	74	1895	70·7	96
			96	73·8	85
1870	73·1	76	97	79·2	72
71	78·1	72	98	72·1	108
72	74·3	63	99	73·1	85
73	74·1	86			
74	71·1	66	1900	76·8	65
			01	73·0	74
1875	72·1	94	02	73·4	101
76	76·4	70	03	74·0	65
77	72·0	66	04	72·9	64
78	72·2	87			
79	75·6	39	1905	71·5	75
			06	74·5	77
1880	75·6	60	07	77·9	49
81	72·6	86	08	72·1	99
82	74·0	93	09	73·8	82
83	71·4	96			
84	75·6	70	1910	73·0	75
			11	75·9	77
1885	70·7	75	12	73·0	83
86	75·0	62	13	72·0	97
			1914	74·0	63

of potatoes in Ohio from 1860 to 1914 and the above exercises may be repeated to examine their relationship.

Simultaneous Influence of Two Climatic Factors on Yield

The foregoing methods are applicable only when it is desired to establish the influence of a single variable on another, but if two influences are at work, e.g. temperature and rainfall, we are faced with the limitations imposed by the two dimensions of the graph paper. We have a three-dimensional problem to face with only two dimensions that we can use. This is the same problem that the cartographer has to face; he negotiates the difficulty by using the contour as a conventional representation of the third dimension (relief) and we may imitate his device by using isopleths.

Ex. If, for example, we are supplied with the rainfall figures, the temperature, and the yield of a crop in some region, over a number of years (or seasons), and the question is asked, 'Are they related?' the method of procedure is as follows.

Using rainfall as ordinates and temperature as abscissae place a figure (the yield for that year) at the appropriate point and repeat the operation for each year. If a consistent relationship exists the figures will fall into a pattern, high yields occurring when temperature and rainfall are most favourable, but the yield falling off in all directions—too dry, too wet, too cold, or too hot. Isopleths are drawn enclosing equal yields. The centre of the enclosed group of highest yields defines the optimum conditions whose temperature and rainfall can be read off. Fig. 60 [1] is an example of this method.

The Detection of Limits Set by Two Interacting Variables

It would be interesting to apply this method to the areas in, for example, those frontier zones in the Middle West where winter wheat, spring wheat and corn are in competition. In the farmer's mind the choice of crop is influenced by, among other things, the realizable yield, which, in turn, is influenced by certain features of the temperature and rainfall régimes. Increasing summer concentration of rain, for example, sways the advantage towards corn and away from wheat.

Crops, of course, are never grown up to their physical limits, though they may be pushed to an economic limit beyond which cultivation does not repay. But a particular type of natural vegetation may spread to its physical limits and there be extinguished, as the last grass or shrubs die away at the ultimate limit of aridity. Elsewhere two types of natural vegetation may be in competition and literally engaged in a struggle for survival; their frontier marks the point where the balance of conditions changes to the advantage of one as against the other.

[1] After Huntington, Williams and Valkenberg.

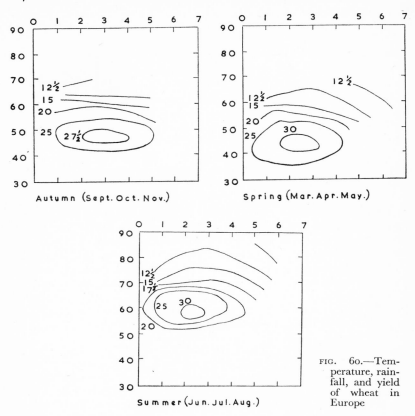

Autumn (Sept. Oct. Nov.)

Spring (Mar. Apr. May.)

Summer (Jun. Jul. Aug.)

FIG. 60.—Temperature, rainfall, and yield of wheat in Europe

Fig. 61 is an example of the application of this method to the examination of the combined influence of mean annual temperature and mean annual rainfall on the natural vegetation. The index letter of the vegetation type at about 160 stations all over the world has been placed at the appropriate intersection. This is a quograph. The quotient $\frac{T}{R} = 5$ appears to coincide with the limit of deserts. The line

$$R = \frac{3T}{4} - 12$$

corresponds to the limit of forests.[1]

The Resultant of Three or More Climatic Elements Considered Simultaneously

Having considered the effect of two variable factors on a third

[1] See A. Austin Miller, 'The Climatic Requirements of some Major Vegetational Formations', *Advancement of Science*, VII, 25 (1950), p. 94.

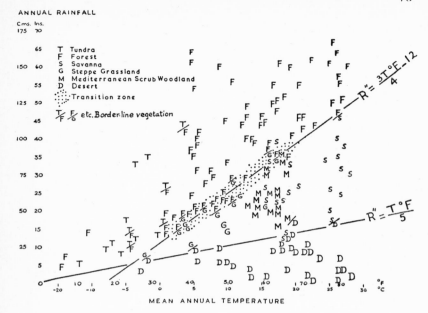

FIG. 61.—Limits of forest, grassland, and desert

(resultant) we may proceed to the examination of still more complicated relationships. The climatic environment is never simple and the reaction of inorganic surfaces, such as buildings, can never be satisfactorily related to any one element of the climate treated in isolation. A corrugated iron roof can become unbearably hot in strong sunshine though the air temperature be quite low; radiant heat, specific heat, and ventilation enter the equation of heat balance. The butter in a wetted porous pot can be kept cool even in hot thirsty air; latent heat of vaporization has an important influence. Living things, plant or animal, feel the combined effect of all the elements to which they are exposed and their reactions are still more complicated and difficult to assess or to predict.

Physical comfort or discomfort, as well as mental state, are partly conditioned by the climate, in the broad sense, either indoors or in the open air, and heating engineers have given much consideration to this difficult subject. It has also engaged the attention of those concerned in the organization of expeditions to regions of climatic discomfort and of the scientific branches of the fighting services.[1] Agronomists and plant physiologists, too, have met the problem in their studies of the

[1] D. H. K. Lee and H. Lemons, 'Clothing for Global Man', *Geog. Rev.*, 39 (1949), pp. 181–213.

relationship of crop yields and the acclimatization of plants introduced to new environments.

One of the many formidable difficulties that attend the quantitative assessment of such influences is the precise measurement of the effect produced. Weight increments, linear growth rates, &c. are measurable quantities, but even with the most careful of controls it is not easy to apportion the credit with certainty to the proper climatic factor or combination of factors.

With animals and humans the quantitative assessment of physical or mental state is still more difficult to make objectively. Some measure of the rate of heat exchange can, however, be calculated from skin temperature which can be used to supplement and check the patient's subjective description of his sensations and symptoms. So, as an example, we may try to assess the influence of the various climatic factors at work in determining physical comfort.

Thermal Environment [1]

The deeper tissues of the human body are maintained, in health, at a temperature of 98·4° F. (normal) by a balance between the generation of heat within and the loss from the skin and lungs. This loss is affected by several qualities of the thermal environment, including

1. Radiation towards bodies of lower temperature.
2. Conduction by the surrounding air.
3. Ventilation by moving air (wind or draught).
4. Evaporation of moisture from skin and lungs.

The sensation of warmth or chill experienced by the body thus depends, not on air temperature alone, but on a number of other factors difficult to measure. The combined effect of 2, 3, and 4 (above) is known as the 'Effective Temperature', and can be assessed by the wet- and dry-bulb thermometer combined with an air current meter.

As a result of careful experiments on patients it has been found that the relationship can be expressed by a chart (cf. nomogram, p. 180). The one reproduced here (Fig. 62) is appropriate for a lightly clothed body.

To use the chart, draw a straight line through the points representing the wet- and dry-bulb temperatures. Where this meets the line representing the velocity of the air read off the effective temperature on the curved near-vertical lines. Without making any extravagant claims to precision it may be said that effective temperatures in excess of blood heat are lethal; 90° is about the limit of endurance for people resting or doing light work; 80° is about the limit for heavy manual

---

[1] 'Environmental Warmth and its Measurement', *Medical Research Council War Memorandum, No. 17*, T. Bedford, H.M.S.O., 1946.

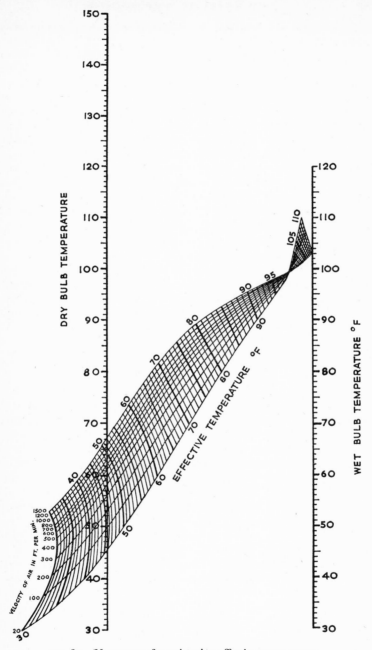

FIG. 62.—Nomogram for estimating effective temperature

labour; between 60° and 80° the efficiency of labour is reduced and the accident rate is liable to rise; below 60° manual dexterity is reduced in people engaged in light work or sedentary occupations.

TABLE 30: *Climatic discomfort in Western Australia*

*		J.	F.	M.	A.	M.	J.	Jy.	A.	S.	O.	N.	D.	Total day-degrees for year
Wyndham 15° S. 128° E.	D.B.	90	89	89	88	85	79	78	82	87	91	92	91	
	W.B.	81	80	79	73	68	64	63	66	71	76	79	77	
	E.T.													
	D.D.													
Halls Creek 18° S. 128° E.	D.B.	89	88	89	81	75	70	68	73	80	87	90	90	
	W.B.	75	74	73	64	59	56	54	57	61	67	70	74	
	E.T.													
	D.D.													
Broome 18° S. 122° E.	D.B.	87	87	87	85	79	74	73	76	80	83	87	88	
	W.B.	79	80	78	73	67	63	61	64	67	71	76	79	
	E.T.													
	D.D.													
Nullagine 22° S. 120° E.	D.B.	93	91	88	81	72	65	63	68	75	83	90	92	
	W.B.	73	73	69	64	58	55	53	55	58	61	66	70	
	E.T.													
	D.D.													
Wiluna 27° S. 120° E.	D.B.	89	88	83	75	65	58	56	60	67	74	83	88	
	W.B.	68	69	66	61	55	50	48	51	55	59	63	67	
	E.T.													
	D.D.													
Kalgoorlie 31° S. 121° E.	D.B.	82	81	76	70	62	56	55	58	63	69	76	81	
	W.B.	67	67	65	60	55	52	50	51	54	57	62	65	
	E.T.													
	D.D.													
Perth 32° S. 116° E.	D.B.	76	77	74	69	63	59	57	58	60	63	69	73	
	W.B.	64	65	63	61	57	55	53	53	54	56	59	62	
	E.T.													
	D.D.													
Rawlinna 31° S. 126° E.	D.B.	78	79	74	69	62	57	55	57	64	69	74	77	
	W.B.	64	67	64	60	55	52	50	51	53	57	61	64	
	E.T.													
	D.D.													

* D.B. = Mean Dry-bulb temperature of working day.
   W.B. =   ,,   Wet- ,,   ,,   ,,   ,,   ,,
   E.T. =   ,,   Effective   ,,   ,,   ,,   ,,
   D.D. = Day-degrees above 69° F.

Ex. With the aid of the nomogram (Fig. 62) complete the table and

Dry bulb	Wet bulb	Air velocity	Effective temp.
115° F.	100° F.	200 ft./minute	
82	80	0	
60	55	120	
60	50	1500	
45	35	400	

comment on the thermal environment for (1) picnic lunch, (2) field sketching, (3) rowing a race.

Accumulated Effective Temperatures

High effective temperatures, long maintained, clearly constitute an uncomfortable condition for engaging in sustained manual work and are particularly arduous for people of European descent. A measure of this adverse quality of a climate may be given by accumulated effective temperatures (cf. p. 137) in excess of an optimum which lies about 70° F.

Ex. From the figures given in Table 30, assuming calm conditions, assess the degree of climatic discomfort during the working day in Western Australia by determining the accumulated effective temperatures in day-degrees above 69° F. for each month and arrive at a total for the year.

The examples just considered have been only remotely connected with water circulation, through the humidity factor, but were introduced here, instead of in the section on temperature, because of the complexity of many factors simultaneously considered. We may now return to the more direct consideration of water in the atmosphere, on the earth's surface and within the crust. This, too, will usually involve the simultaneous consideration and comparison of two or more sets of data.

Section III. Excretion. The Disposal of Water

Evaporation and Temperature

The direct measurement of evaporation (from pans) was considered on p. 159. We may now inquire into the causes of its variation. It is well known that the evaporation of water from lakes and rivers, dew from the grass, or dampness out of clothes proceeds more rapidly at high temperatures than at low; we may inquire whether evaporation is a function of temperature.

Ex. Using the figures supplied (columns 1 and 2 of Table 31) plot

TABLE 31: *Temperature, humidity, and evaporation*

	Camden Square, London					Southport				
	1	2	3	4	5	1	2	3	4	5
Jan.	40	0·1	0·2	81	1·9	40	0·0	0·1	84	2·6
Feb.	41	0·2	0·2	73	1·7	40	0·2	0·1	79	2·1
Mar.	44	0·7	0·7	63	1·8	42	0·7	0·8	71	2·2
Apr.	48	1·5	1·2	62	1·5	46	1·6	1·5	69	1·9
May	56	2·4	2·2	58	1·8	52	2·4	2·5	68	2·1
Jun.	61	2·9	2·8	57	2·0	56	3·1	3·1	68	2·2
Jul.	64	3·0	3·2	57	2·4	60	3·0	(3·8)	71	2·9
Aug.	64	2·3	(3·2)	61	2·2	60	2·3	(3·8)	72	2·5
Sep.	59	1·4	(2·6)	64	1·8	56	1·4	(3·1)	71	2·8
Oct.	52	0·6	(1·7)	70	2·6	50	0·7	(2·1)	75	3·5
Nov.	44	0·3	(0·7)	78	2·4	43	0·2	(1·0)	82	3·1
Dec.	42	0·1	(0·5)	81	2·4	41	0·1	(1·6)	84	3·2

Columns 1. Mean temperature (° F.) to nearest whole degree.
      2. Mean evaporation in inches.
      3. Evaporation calculated from formulae.
      4. Mean relative humidity (%) at 1300 hrs.
      5. Mean rainfall.

evaporation as ordinates against temperature as abscissae, joining the 12 monthly dots for each station to make a 12-sided polygon. Although only two stations have been considered it will already be abundantly clear that evaporation (from tanks) is not a function of mean temperature alone. It will have been discovered from the graph that with comparable temperatures the evaporation rate during the early months of the year, while temperature is rising, is much greater than in the latter half of the year, while temperature is falling. From January to July at London the curve rises steadily in what is nearly a straight line with a formula approximately $E = \dfrac{T}{8} - 5\cdot2$ (see p. 168) but for the second half of the year the graph is bowed and this formula no longer holds good. At Southport for the first six months the graph also approximates to a straight line, but this time with a formula approximately

$$E = \frac{T}{6} - 6 \cdot 2.$$ Here again the graph for the second (falling) half of

the year is a curve far away from the rising line of January to June.

The theoretical values of evaporation, calculated according to these formulae, are set down in column 3 of the table; the agreement in the early months is seen to be quite good; the unsatisfactory values for the 'fall' are shown in brackets. From these exercises it is apparent that the relationship between temperature and evaporation at Southport differs from that at London, and that at both places the relationship is different, and more complex, in autumn than in spring. We may ask ourselves why it is that evaporation is less powerful during the fall. The mists and heavy dews of autumn are everybody's experience and we are inclined to associate them with humid air and a high dew-point, which in turn is the consequence of a high relative humidity.

Ex. To examine whether the explanation is to be found here we may test whether evaporation is a function of relative humidity, and for this purpose the R.H. at 1300 hours is given in column 4 of the table. Disappointed in this we may next examine whether evaporation is a combined function of temperature and relative humidity by the means described on pp. 171–2. If no pattern emerges from this study we can still try combinations with other elements in the Book of Normals that might be expected to influence evaporation, e.g. relative humidity at 0700 hours and 1800 hours, vapour pressure, moisture content, wind force, &c.

It is to be feared that the most noteworthy success of these exercises will be to demonstrate the incompetence of any of these combinations to provide a simple way of computing the probable evaporation.

Evaporation and Rainfall

But having tried all the likely factors let us consider an unlikely one, namely rainfall. It is not easy to see why the amount of rain falling in a month should affect the rate of evaporation from a water surface (except while the rain is actually falling), but it has been claimed that the ratio of precipitation to evaporation at a place can be calculated from a formula based on precipitation and temperature.

$$\frac{P}{E} = 11 \cdot 5 \left(\frac{P}{T - 10} \right)^{\frac{10}{9}} \ [1]$$

For the purpose of testing the applicability of this formula to Camden

---

[1] C. W. Thornthwaite, *Geog. Rev.*, 1931, p. 639.

Square and Southport the monthly rainfall figures are given in column 5 of Table 31.

Ex. Plot precipitation as ordinates and temperature as abscissae, placing the corresponding value of evaporation at the appropriate point for each month at both stations. See whether a coherent pattern emerges; if it does analyse the pattern. Fig. 63 shows the pattern that would appear if the above formula holds good; it could be used as a nomogram (see p. 174) for calculating evaporation on this basis.

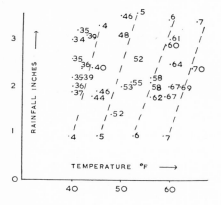

FIG. 63.—Mean monthly evaporation values at Campden Hill and Southport, calculated from the formula

$$E = \cfrac{P}{11.5\left(\cfrac{P}{T-10}\right)\cfrac{10}{9}}$$

Effective Rainfall

It is well known, and a fact of great agricultural, biological, and geographical importance, that the value and efficiency of rainfall, inch for inch, differs from place to place. The two most important underlying factors are

1. the nature of occurrence of the rain, as steady falls or as torrential 'thunder' rain; this affects the rate of percolation or of run-off;
2. the temperature of the air, which presumably affects the proportion lost by re-evaporation.

Let us examine these in turn. The nature of occurrence of rain is a value that is not reported from climatological stations, but a measure of the mean intensity of fall can be arrived at by dividing the mean monthly rainfall by the number of days on which a measurable amount of rain falls (the rain day). The data for Table 32 are obtained from the various volumes of the *Handbuch der Klimatologie*. They range over a wide variety of climatic types and seasons.

Ex. Enter the precipitation per rain day in the vacant column. In addition to showing how wide is the variation of daily doses of rain in different climates the results convey certain hints, such that at Paris, while days with rain are not quite as frequent in July as in January, each one brings much heavier rain. In the Mediterranean climates of

TABLE 32: *Effective rainfall*

Station	Month	Precipitation	Rain days	Precipitation, mm. per Rain day	Temp., ° C.
Bulawayo	Jan.	137	15		22
	Oct.	16	5		22
Beira	Feb.	269	19		27
	Sept.	23	3		23
Auckland, N.Z.	Jan.	65	10		19
Perth	Jan.	9	3		23
	Jun.	176	17		14
Alice Springs	Nov.	25	4		26
Brisbane	Mar.	141	15		24
	Aug.	50	7		16
Sydney	Jul.	118	12		12
Darwin	Feb.	342	20		29
	Oct.	50	5		30
Bangkok	Apr.	43	5		29
	Sept.	302	22		28
Batavia	Jan.	270	22		25
	Jul.	72	8		26
Baguio	Aug.	1197	27		18
Paris	Jan.	35	14		2
	Jul.	50	12		18
Zurich	Jan.	46	11		− 1
	Jul.	133	15		18
Vienna	Feb.	36	5		− 2
	Jun.	79	10		19
Hamburg	Jan.	48	16		0
	Jul.	86	16		17
Warsaw	Jan.	33	15		− 3
	Jul.	77	15		18
Athens	Jan.	54	12		9
	Jul.	7	2		27
Salonika	Jan.	36	6		5
	Jul.	24	4		27
Madrid	Mar.	43	10		8
	Aug.	13	3		25
Turin	Jan.	56	7		0
	Jul.	59	10		23

Perth and Athens it is the winter day that brings more rain. But clearly something is lacking here for a proper assessment of intensity; the figures give no information as to the duration of the rain (in hours or minutes) on each rain day. Such figures are difficult to obtain, but Table 33 gives the data for some British stations.

Ex. Complete rows 4, 5, and 6. Compare the values in column 4 with the figures supplied for drawing a graph on p. 166.

TABLE 33: *Rainfall; intensity, duration, incidence*

	Valencia						London (Camden Square)					
	1	2	3	4	5	6	1	2	3	4	5	6
Jan.	5·5	24	96				1·9	15	43			
Feb.	5·2	21	62				1·7	13	39			
Mar.	4·5	21	71				1·8	14	44			
Apr.	3·7	19	50				1·5	13	31			
May	3·2	18	57				1·8	13	29			
June	3·2	17	73				2·0	12	30			
July	3·8	21	62				2·4	12	27			
Aug.	4.8	22	73				2·2	14	28			
Sept.	4·1	18	64				1·8	11	25			
Oct.	5·6	22	78				2·6	15	45			
Nov.	5·5	23	89				2·4	15	47			
Dec.	6·6	26	100				2·4	16	49			

1. Average rainfall (inches).
2. Number of rain days.
3. Average duration of rain (in hours).
4. Average intensity of rain (hundredths of an inch per hour).
5. Average daily duration of rain per rain day.
6. Average rainfall per rain day.

Evapo-transpiration

Evaporation goes on not only from water surfaces but from all surfaces and interstices to which water and air have access. Soil water passes upwards by capillarity renewing the surface moisture as it is evaporated. The form of the ground and the texture of the soil are clearly involved. But the direct evaporation of water into the air is not the only medium of water loss; the plant cover, grass, crops, shrubs or trees, act as additional channels through which moisture is transpired, fast or slow according to weather and soil conditions.

The combined rate of loss is a very difficult thing to measure empirically or to calculate theoretically; two courageous attempts, to which every serious student should refer, are:

1. C. W. Thornthwaite, 'An Approach Towards a Rational Classification of Climate', *Geog. Rev.* 38 (1948), pp. 55–94.
2. H. L. Penman, *Proc. Roy. Soc., A*, 193 (1948), p. 120.

Percolation

A seepage gauge consists of a cylinder enclosing a column of undisturbed soil, 11 in. in depth. No run-off occurs because the surface is flat, so that the difference between the measured rainfall and the amount of water that passes through the gauge is assumed to have been evaporated. Percolation measurements are recorded in *British Rainfall*, from which the following are taken.

TABLE 34: *Drainage observations at Prescot, Lancs.*

1948	Rainfall	Seepage gauges		% loss	
		Bare soil	Turfed soil	Bare soil	Turfed soil
Jan.	6·85	6·43	6·45		
Feb.	1·99	1·51	1·49		
Mar.	0·80	0·00	0·00		
Apr.	1·28	0·01	0·07		
May	1·58	0·04	0·00		
Jun.	3·83	1·55	0·50		
Jul.	2·43	1·20	0·62		
Aug.	4·23	1·44	1·15		
Sept.	1·68	0·25	0·22		
Oct.	2·66	1·09	1·16		
Nov.	1·96	1·66	1·73		
Dec.	3·18	2·63	2·64		
Year	32·47	17·81	16·03		
Calculated evaporation (by difference)		14·66	16·44		

Ex. Draw block graphs to show percolation below the line, and the balance of rainfall (evaporation, &c.) above the line. Calculate the percentage evaporated and (in the case of turfed soil) transpired and plot as line graphs. Compare the seasonal variations in the two columns and account for the difference.

Catchment Areas

The 'general rainfall' of a region is defined as the mean depth at which the rain of a given period would stand, assuming it to remain as it fell. If, in a catchment area, there were an abundance of rain-gauges, evenly distributed, the mean of all the individual rainfalls would be the required general rainfall. In practice, however, few regions can claim to be adequately provided with rain-gauges, and there is little likelihood of a regular distribution. The determination of general rainfall must therefore be based either on the records of a few stations selected as being representative of different parts of the basin: or, and more scientifically, on a reasonably accurate picture of the distribution of rainfall over the whole basin, which can be derived from all the available records.

An example of the latter method has been provided by H. R. Mill.[1] The stages are as follows.

    1. From all available data, construct an isohyetal map of the river basin. (It is assumed that the limits of the basin have been accurately determined and drawn.)

    2. Measure the areas of the zones between successive isohyets.

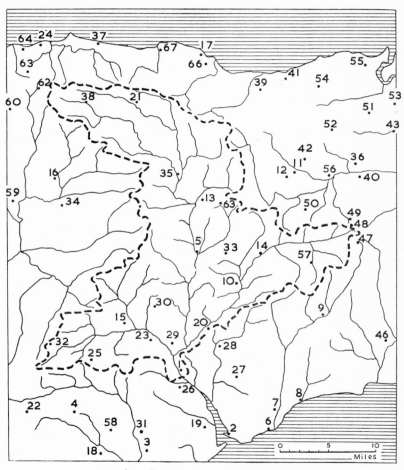

FIG. 64.—Catchment area of the River Exe

[1] R.G.S., *Final Report on the Investigation of Rivers*, 1916.

3. Multiply the area of each zone by the mean rainfall of the zone (i.e. the mean of the values of the two isohyets bounding it): this calculation gives the volume of rainfall on each zone.

4. Add all the volumes together, and divide by the total area of the basin: the result is the general rainfall in inches per annum.

Ex. Table 35 gives the average annual rainfalls of 67 stations in and near the Exe basin, for the 10-year period 1898–1907. Use the outline map of Fig. 64 on which these stations are marked, to determine the general rainfall over the Exe basin during that period. It should be noted that rainfall stations *outside* the river basin are essential to the construction of the isohyetal map. The isohyet interval should be chosen after inspection of the range of rainfall amounts involved. An interval of 5 in. would be suitable in this case.

For the measurement of area, a grid of squares, appropriate to the scale of the map, should be drawn on tracing paper, and the squares, and fractions of squares, counted up. A scale of ¼ in. to 1 mile is generally convenient, each square of ¼-in. side then representing 1 square mile.

TABLE 35: *Rainfall in the neighbourhood of the River Exe—means for 1898–1907*

	Alt., ft.	Rainfall
1. Exeter, Manston Terrace	165	29·2
2. Exmouth, Nidderdale	51	27·2
3. Chudleigh, Ideford	300	34·4
4. Moretonhampstead	600	41·6
5. Tiverton, Ivy Place	270	37·4
6. Budleigh Salterton, Ravenshaw . . .	50	29·2
7. E. Budleigh, Bioton	90	29·6
8. Sidmouth, Sidmount	149	30·2
9. Honiton, Combe Raleigh	500	36·6
10. Callompton	202	33·7
11. Milverton, Olands	330	34·2
12. Milverton, Spring Grove	500	35·0
13. Bampton, Wonham	530	39·2
14. Uffculme, Bullmoor	280	34·2
15. Crediton, Okefield	325	32·5
16. South Molton	450	44·9
17. Minehead	50	32·9
18. Bovey Tracey, Colehays	415	46·4
19. Kenton, Southtown House	56	34·0
20. Siverton, Killerton	161	28·5
21. Exford, North Ley	1000	46·9
22. Chagford, Frenchbeare	950	56·6
23. Newton, St. Cyres	145	31·5
24. Lynton, Lee Abbey	320	38·1
25. Cheriton Bishop	575	32·4
26. Exeter, Ide	90	36·1
27. Aglesbeare, Rosamondford	220	31·6
28. Broad Clyst, Brockhill	80	28·4
29. Upton Pyne	213	33·1

	Alt., ft.	Rainfall
30. Stockleigh Pomeroy	340	33·0
31. Torquay Waterworks, Trusham . . .	322	36·3
32. Spregton	735	34·1
33. Halberton	240	34·0
34. Romansleigh	590	37·1
35. Exbridge	400	42·6
36. Taunton, Staplegrove	108	29·6
37. Lynmouth, Glenthorne	93	46·1
38. Simonsbath	1080	66·5
39. Williton, Aller Farm	190	33·8
40. Taunton, Linden Grove	70	27·3
41. Quantockshead, St. Audries	250	28·0
42. Halse, The Mount	254	32·1
43. North Petherton	122	29·5
44. Pawlett	45	27·7
45. Kilmington, Hadden Corner	400	35·5
46. Chard, Tatworth	347	40·4
47. Otterford, Otterhead	735	37·6
48. Blagdon Hill Reservoir	588	35·9
49. Leigh Court	350	33·3
50. Wellington, The Avenue	254	30·4
51. Enmore Park	268	30·3
52. Cothelstone, House	500	32·3
53. Bridgwater	30	27·3
54. Holford, Woodlands House	391	32·7
55. Stockland Bristol	65	27·9
56. Allerford, Lynch Mead	100	32·4
57. Dunkerswell Abbey	800	39·1
58. Torquay Waterworks, Bullaton . . .	928	42·3
59. Chittlehamholt	500	38·2
60. Bratton Fleming	—	52·6
61. Stoke Rivers	767	44·7
62. Challacombe	825	63·4
63. Paracombe	795	50·0
64. Martinhoe	808	44·9
65. Huntsham Court	640	42·5
66. Dunster, Allcombe	85	29·4
67. Porlock, Bassington	44	32·3

River Flow: Rating Curves

The discharge of a river is given in cusecs. (cubic feet per second) or in gallons per hour or per day.[1] To measure this it is necessary to know (1) the velocity of flow, measured with a current meter, (2) the cross-sectional area of water (the wetted perimeter). For gauging purposes this is best done over a flat weir which gives an easily measured cross-sectional area, but the surveyed cross-section of the bed, though more clumsy in use, will do. An increase in discharge, due probably to heavy rain, is met by an increase in both velocity and in depth, which enlarges the cross-section.

Ex. Note that the form of the cross-section of the stream bed and (in times of flood) of the valley govern the relationship between depth and cross-sectional area. For each increase in depth of 1 ft. measure

[1] 1 million gals. per day = 1·86 cusecs. or 1 cusec. = 0·538 million gals. per day. For conversions see quograph on p. 116.

the cross-section of the diagrammatic channels shown in Fig. 65 and plot cross-sectional area against depth.

When the discharge has been measured over a considerable period of time and the depth (stage) of the river simultaneously noted on a height gauge a relationship is found to exist between stage and discharge which can be shown on a graph known as a 'rating curve'. If the velocity of discharge remained constant the curves just drawn for Fig. 65 would be rating curves. But, of course, the velocity increases in flood time and the discharge consequently goes up more rapidly than the increase in cross-section.

Both factors, namely increase in cross-section and increase in velocity as the water rises, give to a typical rating curve a form which, plotted

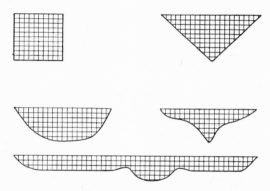

FIG. 65.—Cross-sectional area of stream beds

on rectangular co-ordinates, is normally convex upwards. When the stream overflows its banks on to the flood plain there is only a very slow increase in height for a great increase in discharge (e.g. 5 in Fig. 65); the rating curve is said to be 'non-sensitive' in these ranges. For these reasons it is often preferable to use logarithmic paper, by means of which a better shape is obtained for the rating curve.

Ex. Tables 36 and 37 provide the data for the construction of two rating curves of different form, the latter (Wallkill River) being peculiar in showing an upward concavity in part of the graph, known as a 'reversal'. This could be detected by completing the difference column on the table; the rate of increase in discharge per unit rise in level shows a temporary diminution in place of the usual steady increase. It is due to the ponding up of water by an obstruction or narrowing of the channel downstreams from the gauging point.

Table 36: *River Spey at Loggan Bridge*

Water level, ft.	.0	.1	.2	.3	.4	.5	.6	.7	.8	.9
										Discharge in cusecs, for each tenth of a foot of water level
0				40	43	49	59	74	95	121
1	153	191	234	284	339	402	471	543	620	698
2	779	860	947	1041	1136	1232	1332	1435	1539	1645
3	1754	1864	1975	2090	2205	2320	2440	2560	2690	2820
4	2950	3085	3220	3355	3500	3645	3790	3935	4075	4215
5	4345	4475	4600	4720	4840	4955	5070	5180	5290	5400
6	5510	5620	5730	5840	5950	6060	6170	6280	6390	6500
7	6610									

Table 37: *Wallkill River near Unionville, New York*

Feet	Cusecs.	Diff.	Feet	Cusecs.	Diff.	Feet	Cusecs.	Diff.
4·0	8		6·5	440		9·0	1100	
4·5	65		7·0	530		9·5	1200	
5·0	200		7·5	630		10·0	1600	
5·5	280		8·0	750		10·5	2000	
6·0	360		8·5	900		11·0	2500	

Fluctuation of River Flow

The daily fluctuation of the Severn, given in Table 38, presents an example of a flood rising and subsiding.

Ex. Column graphs are the best method of plotting the data of day-to-day (or month-to-month or year-to-year) variation, since each figure represents an average for the day and not a momentary value. The variability of flow, which is considerable, could be demonstrated by a dispersion graph (cf. p. 130), and analysed and expressed as a percentage (cf. p. 155).

TABLE 38: *Daily discharge in cusecs. of River Severn at Bewdley, January 1934*

1. 690	6. 1790	11. 1546	16. 6350	21. 6230	26. 1790
2. 830	7. 1380	12. 1620	17. 5750	22. 3930	27. 1790
3. 980	8. 1790	13. 3820	18. 5990	23. 2900	28. 1700
4. 980	9. 2150	14. 3600	19. 7240	24. 2300	29. 1620
5. 1300	10. 1790	15. 6740	20. 7500	25. 2150	30. 1380
					31. 1380

Run-off

The volume of rainwater accumulating in a given basin is obviously the area of catchment multiplied by the depth of rain. This rainwater makes its way downhill and downstream; some is lost by evaporation and transpiration, some soaks into the ground, the balance, reinforced by springs, &c. is discharged by the trunk stream into the sea; this is the run-off measured at gauging stations.

The Thames is gauged at Teddington Weir and records of its flow are available from 1883. Some water is abstracted for the supply of suburban areas above the weir and returns to the river below it, this quantity is added to that passing over the weir and their sum is the 'natural flow' to which the Thames Conservancy's data refer. To compare rainfall and run-off it is necessary to convert to the same units either cusecs. or inches; an example of the use of each will be given below.

The discharge, given in cusecs., can be converted to cusecs. per square mile by dividing the cusecs. by the area of the basin (3812 square miles), e.g. mean discharge October 1932: 3312 cusecs. =

$$\frac{3312}{3812} = 0.869 \text{ cusecs. per square mile.}$$

This figure can be converted to inches of run-off by multiplying by:

0·3719 for periods of 1 day
1·041 ,, ,, ,, 28 days (Feb.)
1·079 ,, ,, ,, 29 ,, (Leap Year, Feb.)
1·116 ,, ,, ,, 30 ,, (Apr. Jun. Sept. Nov.)

TABLE 39: *Rainfall and run-off, River Thames at Teddington*

	1933			1934			1935			1936			4-year mean		
	R	R-O	%	R	R-O	%	R	R-O	%	R	R-O	%	R	R-O	%
J.	2·12	1·13		2·19	0·4		0·75	0·86		4·29	3·03				
F.	3·59	1·36		0·25	0·27		2·85	0·77		2·17	2·05				
M.	3·04	2·70		2·33	0·47		0·53	0·81		1·89	1·50				
A.	1·17	0·89		2·09	0·37		3·83	0·97		1·73	1·18				
M.	1·93	0·71		0·71	0·25		1·33	0·53		0·74	0·64				
J.	1·90	0·39		1·35	0·15		4·15	0·51		3·22	0·52				
Jy.	1·73	0·30		1·58	0·13		0·81	0·26		4·32	0·54				
A.	0·77	0·21		2·21	0·14		2·28	0·19		0·60	0·39				
S.	2·83	0·23		2·07	0·14		4·42	0·28		3·33	0·39				
O.	2·05	0·27		1·67	0·16		3·84	0·79		1·72	0·36				
N.	1·01	0·28		2·03	0·22		5·25	2·08		3·23	1·00				
D.	0·47	0·24		6·60	1·16		3·41	1·62		2·76	1·26				
Year	18·31	3·12		31·25	2·69		34·79	14·69		32·66	16·02				
(Oct.–Sept.)	(1933–34)			(1934–35)			(1935–36)			(1936–37)					

1·153 for periods of 31 days (other months)
13·57   „   „   „ 365 „   (year)
13·61   „   „   „ 366 „   (Leap Year)

e.g. 0·869 cusecs. per square mile (Oct. 1932)
0·869 × 1·153 = 1·00 in. of rainfall

Ex. In the following table this has been done and the run-off (R-O) is given in equivalent inches; the rainfall (R) is the general rainfall (inches) over the area as defined above (p. 183). Calculate the percentage of the rainfall running off at Teddington for each month and enter in the blank columns.

It will be found that the run-off occasionally exceeds the rainfall of the month, e.g. January 1935, which carried away some of the excessive rainfall of Dec. 1934.

Ex. This lag is expectable. It may be detected by superimposed column graphs of monthly R and R-O.

The Evaporation Factor in Run-off

Ex. The small proportion of the rainfall that runs off in the summer months is mainly due to evaporation loss. To test, very roughly, whether there is any correlation, plot the short (4 year) mean monthly value (last column, Table 39) against the evaporation data for Camden Square given in table on p. 178.

Rainfall and River Discharge

Table 40 gives the annual rainfall and annual discharge of the River Severn at Worcester, both in cusecs. in this case, and also the rainfall and discharge for summer and winter half years.

TABLE 40: *Mean rates of rainfall and discharge (in cusecs.) of River Severn at Worcester*

Date	Whole year		Summer		Winter	
	R	D	R	D	R	D
1882	6354	3249	5739	2049	7274	4033
1883	4935	2229	4324	1209	5552	3517
1884	4170	1779	3487	921	4182	2423
1885	4932	2152	4732	1172	5542	3402
1886	5806	2779	3806	2006	5255	3107
1887	3514	1615	3309	932	3483	2329
1888	4277	1889	4479	1568	4525	3674
1889	4490	2056	5140	1618		

Ex. Fig. 66 shows them plotted against each other in the way previously used for studying the relationship between two variables (p. 167). Taking, first, the summer conditions, the best-fit curve (pecked line) is slightly bowed, but is not very far from the straight line (drawn full) whose formula is $D = \dfrac{R}{2} - 900$. Turning to the winter figures, apart from an aberrant point (1888) the remainder fall near the line $D = \dfrac{R}{2} + 500$. The results for the whole year (like those of summer) are

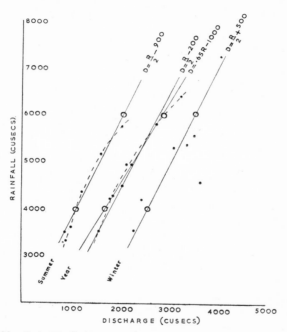

FIG. 66.—Rainfall–discharge relationship. River Severn at Bridgnorth

best suited by a curve; but the best straight-line formula is $D = 0 \cdot 65R - 1,000$. It is, however, not far from the curve $D = \dfrac{R}{2} - 200$.

The discharge may therefore be said to be approximately half the rainfall, plus 500 cusecs. in winter, minus 900 in summer and minus 200 for the year as a whole. The missing cusecs. are, of course, accounted for by percolation, evaporation, and transpiration. The high rate of the last two factors in summer accounts for the low discharge and low level of the river at this season.

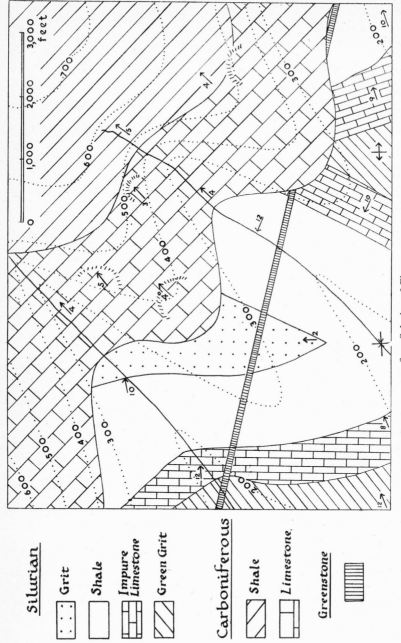

FIG. 67.—Solution of Fig. 17

Silurian

Grit

Shale

Impure
Limestone

Green Grit

Carboniferous

Shale

Limestone

Greenstone

TABLE 41: *Coefficients of flow of some typical rivers*

	J.	F.	M.	A.	M.	J.	Jy.	A.	S.	O.	N.	D.
Rhone, Gletsch	0·1	0·1	0·1	0·2	0·7	2·0	3·6	2·9	1·7	0·7	0·2	0·1
Reuss, Andermatt	0·2	0·2	0·2	0·4	1·6	2·7	2·5	1·7	1·1	0·7	0·4	0·3
Seine, Paris	1·7	2·0	1·7	1·3	0·8	0·5	0·5	0·4	0·6	0·7	0·8	1·2
Blue Nile, Atbara	0	0	0	0	0	0	1·9	6·0	3·3	0·8	0·2	0
Tiber, Rome	1·2	1·3	1·4	1·4	1·2	0·8	0·6	0·6	0·6	0·7	1·1	1·2
Drac, Sautet	0·4	0·5	0·6	1·2	1·9	2·0	1·1	0·7	0·7	1·0	1·2	0·8
Ardèche, Vallon	1·2	1·3	1·5	1·4	1·9	0·4	0·2	0·2	0·5	1·4	1·7	1·5

TABLE 42: *Seasonal regime of rivers (stage height in metres)*

	J.	F.	M.	A.	M.	J.	Jy.	A.	S.	O.	N.	D.
Rhine at:												
Strasbourg	2·5	2·5	2·7	3·0	3·4	3·9	3·8	3·6	3·3	3·0	2·8	2·7
Mannheim	3·9	3·8	4·0	4·2	4·6	5·1	5·0	4·8	4·4	4·0	3·8	4·0
Mainz	1·4	1·5	1·6	1·6	1·7	2·0	1·9	1·8	1·5	1·3	1·3	1·5
Coblenz	2·8	2·9	3·0	2·8	2·8	3·0	2·9	2·7	2·5	2·4	2·5	2·9
Emmerich	2·8	2·8	2·7	2·4	2·3	2·5	2·4	2·1	1·9	1·8	2·0	2·8
Danube at:												
Dillingen	0·2	0·4	0·3	0·5	0·4	0·3	0·2	0·1	0·1	0·0	0·0	0·1
Linz	0·5	0·8	1·0	1·3	1·5	1·8	1·7	1·5	1·3	0·8	0·8	0·7
Vienna	1·1	1·1	1·2	1·6	1·8	2·0	1·9	1·7	1·3	0·9	0·8	0·8
Pest	1·5	2·1	2·2	2·7	2·8	2·9	2·7	2·6	2·1	1·6	1·5	1·6
Orsova	2·1	2·5	3·1	3·7	3·8	3·4	2·9	2·4	2·1	1·9	2·4	2·5
Nile at:						*(Monthly coefficients)*						
Ripon Falls	0·9	0·9	0·9	1·0	1·2	1·2	1·1	1·0	1·0	0·9	0·9	1·0
Mongalla	0·9	0·8	0·8	0·8	0·9	1·0	1·1	1·2	1·3	1·2	1·1	1·0
Khartum (White Nile)	1·1	0·9	0·7	0·7	0·7	0·8	0·7	0·7	1·3	1·7	1·5	1·3
Wadi Halfa	0·5	0·4	0·3	0·2	0·2	0·2	0·6	2·5	3·1	2·1	1·1	0·7

Régime of Rivers: Coefficient of Flow

The data may be presented either in the form of volume of discharge or of height of water, the one is convertible to the other by the stage-discharge diagram or rating curve. When analysing the seasonal variation (régime) we are concerned with the shape of the graph of mean monthly flow and not with the actual volume of discharge, so it is often more convenient to express the monthly flow in the form of a ratio (cf. pluviometric coefficients, p. 159). Thus if the yearly mean flow is 3,000 cusecs. and the January mean flow is 6,000 then the coefficient for January is $\frac{6}{3} = 2$. And if the July flow is 2,000 cusecs. then the July coefficient is $\frac{2000}{3000}$ or 0·67.

Ex. The examples given in Table 41 may be plotted as line graphs. The influence of the following factors may be detected.

1. Glacier melt water; midsummer maximum, e.g. Rhone.
2. Snow melt; maximum when temperature rises above freezing, e.g. Volga.
3. Maximum in rainy season (when temperature varies little), e.g. Blue Nile.
4. Minimum due to evaporation in hot season (when rainfall varies little), e.g. Seine.
5. Marked minimum when hot season corresponds to dry season, e.g. Tiber.

The curves for the Drac and the Ardèche provide examples of compound régimes where two factors produce two maxima at different times of the year.

Ex. Many rivers pass through two or more régimes during a long course, and high water is experienced at different times in different parts of the course. Explanations based on the general principles stated above should be found for the régimes listed in Tables 41 and 42.

POSTSCRIPT

IF it should be thought that the austere and unemotional tone of the exercises in this book have dehumanized the study of geography, the simple answer is that human geography begins where this book ends. It could be said, without injustice, that ways have been sought of defining and describing the anatomy and physiology of a sleeping landscape. Colour, expression and the personality that reveals itself in the life and movement that goes on upon its surface have found no place in what has been no more than an objective investigation of the form and function of the outer skin of the earth. It has analysed the physique, to which the cultural features add personality, a much more elusive quality of landscape and one which is less amenable to precise quantitative treatment. But since geography concerns itself with the link between man and place, nothing less than the fullest analysis of the physical background of place will serve for the examination of the bond between man and his environment. In effectiveness it ranges from sheer compulsion at the one extreme to virtual freedom of choice at the other. The link may often appear to be too obvious to be worth testing, but may turn out to be subtler and more complex than at first appeared, or it may be so tenuous that only the most refined methods will detect its existence. In either case to neglect or to scamp such analysis and to hurry on content with a few shallow remarks based on perfunctory observation of the physical elements of the environment may result in overlooking or in falsifying the natural intimacy of relation that nearly always exists between the physical and the cultural landscape. To illuminate, to clarify and, as far as is possible, to give precision to this relationship is the geographer's task, for which the map, giving a synoptic view of the distribution of things both physical and human, is the most valuable tool. The analysis of the physical landscape, however thorough, is not the end of map interpretation; it is only the end of the beginning.

INDEX

This index does not include titles to be found in the lists of sections, figures and tables on pp. viii–x.

Accumulated temperature, 137 et seq., 177
Adiabats, 106 et seq.
Age of structures, determination of, 33
Aldershot sheet, 24
Amazon, River, 74
Amplitude of relief, 61–3
Andesite, 41
Atlantic Ocean, winds of, 118
Average slope, 46 et seq.
Aylesbury sheet (geological), 15

Bandon River, 78
Barrell, J., 58
Basalt, 40
Base level, 61, 65
Ben Nevis sheet, 36
— — temperatures, 136
Blackwater, River, 74, 78
Block diagrams, 78 et seq.
Brampton sheet, 24, 36

Catchment basin, 183
Causses, 76
Chalk, 41
Charnwood Forest, 39
Chesterfield sheet, 24
Cheviot sheet, 36
Chiltern Hills, 39, 63–5
Cirencester sheet, 15, 24
Clay, 41
Climatic data, sources, 113
— —, limitations, 114
Climographs, 163
Coastal plateaux, 63, 65, 66
Coefficient of flow in rivers, 195
Colorado, River, 74
Condensation level (cloud-base), 111
Conglomerate, 41
Congo, River, 74
Contours, 43
— , construction of, 44
Conversion tables, 115
Corn yield and climate, 166 et seq.
Crest-line profile, 56
Cusecs, 116, 117, 186

Daily Aerological Record, 107
Daily Weather Report, 96
Dartmoor sheet, 36
Day-degrees, 137
Deviation, mean and standard, 142
Dew-point, 110, 165
Dip, 13 et seq.
Dip faults, 25
Discharge of rivers, 186 et seq.

Dispersion graph, 130, 154
Divides, pattern of, 77
Dover Coalfield, 33
Drainage pattern, 74
Drift maps, 10, 13
Dykes, 36

Edinburgh sheet, 24
Equipluves, 159
Evaporation, 159 et seq.
Evapo-transpiration, 182
Exe, River Basin, general rainfall, 184

Facet maps, 72
Falmouth sheet, 36
Field mapping, 34, 35
Form lines, 43
Formula for straight line, 168
Fort William, temperature at, 136
Frequency of phenomena, 146
Fronts, movement of, 105
Frost days, 146
Frost-free period, 142

Geological maps, 9 et seq.
— survey, 9, 10
— succession, 11
Geostrophic wind scale, 102, 103
Gneiss, 40
Goring gap, 78
Gradient, 46 et seq.
Granite, 40
Gravel, 41
Growing season, 135–44

Hachures, 43
Hade of fault, 30
Harrogate, evaporation at, 160
Henley-on-Thames sheet, 15
Hog's Back, 33
Hollingworth, S. E., 58
Humidity, relative, 165
Hungerford sheet, 24
Hydrographic cycle, 148
Hythergraphs, 58

Isanomalies of temperature, 125
Isle of Wight sheet, 24, 33
Isobars, 100 et seq.
Isonephs and Isohels, 118

Karstic drainage, 76
Kennet, River, 16, 74
Kettering sheet, 15
Killing frost, 140
Knick point, 51, 53

Laccoliths, 36
Lake District, superimposed profiles, 58
— —, drainage and divides, 78
Lava flows, 36
Lee, River, 78
Limestone, 41
— drainage, 76
Limits, comparison of, 138

Marl, 42
'Maturity', in landscape, 49
—, in river, 51
Mawddach Estuary, 61
Medway, River, 74
Month-degrees, 138

Nile, River, 74, 76, 77
Nomogram, 174, 180

Ouse, River, Great, 74
—, —, Yorkshire, 74
Outcrop, 17 et seq.
Overlap, 32
Owenashad, River, 55

Penzance sheet, 37
Percolation, 183
Petersfield (Hants), evaporation at, 160
Phacolites, 86
Physical comfort and climate, 174
Plugs (volcanic), 36
Pluviometric coefficient, 159
Practical work, 5
Pre-Triassic surface, 39
Profile, 49
Projected profiles, 57

Quartzite, 40
Quograph, 116

Radio soundings, 107
Rainfall, discontinuities, 154
—, duration, 182
—, effective, 180, 181
—, intensity, 182
—, mean, mode and median, 152
—, seasonal distribution, 155
—, short period records, 149–52
—, variability, 155
Rating curve, 187 et seq.
Reading, rainfall at, 151
—, sheet, 15
—, temperature, 130
Régime of rivers, 195
Regions, 3
Reversal of rating curve, 187
Rhymney, River, 62
Rhyolite, 41
Run-off, 186 et seq

Sand, 41
Sandstone, 41
Scale, exaggeration of, 28
Schooley peneplain, 56
Section drawing, 28
Severn, River, discharge, 189, 191
Shale, 41
Shannon, River, 74
Slate, 41
Spey, River, discharge, 188
Spur profiles, 60
Stability (atmosphere), 110
Stage, of river, 187
— in erosion, 49
Station model (weather maps), 92
Stoke-on-Trent sheet, 24
Stream bed cross-sectional area, 187
Strike, 13 et seq.
— faults, 24
sub-Eocene surface, 39, 49
Sunshine, 120 et seq.
Symbols on weather maps, 92 et seq.

Tavy, River, 53
Temperature, accumulated, 137
—, annual march of, 134, 135
—, anomalies, 125
—, daily maximum and minimum, 131
—, dispersion graph, 130 et seq.
—, hourly variations, 135, 136
—, range of, 123, 134
—, upper air, 121
Tephigram, 106
Texture of dissection, 75
Thalweg, 50
Thames, River, discharge, 189, 190
Thermal environment, 174
Three-point maps, 21
Thunder, frequency of, 147
Tree line, 139
Tropopause, 110, 123

Unconformity, 13, 25, 31, 39
Units and scales, 115 et seq.

Valencia (Ireland), sunshine, 121
Valley forms, 49

Wallkill, River, discharge, 188
Water gaps, 60
Wheat yield and rainfall, 168
Wind gaps, 60, 78
Wind, constancy and direction, 118
Witney sheet, 15
Wye, River, 51, 52

Yield, and one climatic element, 166 et seq.
—, and two climatic elements, 171